America the Menace

Scenes from the Life of the Future

AMERICA THE MENACE

Scenes from the Life of the Future

BY

GEORGES DUHAMEL

TRANSLATED BY

CHARLES MINER THOMPSON

BOSTON AND NEW YORK
HOUGHTON MIFFLIN COMPANY
The Riverside Press Cambridge
1931

The Riverside Press
CAMBRIDGE · MASSACHUSETTS
PRINTED IN THE U.S.A.

PREFACE

Of all the tasks common to the men of my time none is more urgent than that of incessantly reviewing and correcting the idea of civilization.

Last year in a solid and brilliant discourse Ernst Robert Curtius tried to prove that in France 'the idea of nation' and 'the idea of civilization' were identical, and that since the war the most disinterested and liberal effort made by the French in this field of thought is that of the men who aim at divorcing our conception of civilization from the national ideology in order to expand it so as to include Europe at least.

There is no one in Germany better able to apply to French affairs a sane, flexible, and well-informed judgment than Curtius. I accordingly feel great regret in finding that I disagree with him. Since 1900, the ideal of civilization has doubtless met with various adventures in 'French consciousness.' In my opinion the most noteworthy of them are not those which Curtius detects and emphasizes.

If, at the outbreak of the war, I had not yet tasted the bitter fruit of maturity, I had nevertheless long since received my education, and had taken on my shoulders that burden of servitudes which is called independence, and I had already tested the general ideas that were mine by right of inheritance or of conquest. In the hospitals and in the laboratories, I was living in the society of men for whom civilization represented, not merely a European inheritance, but an inheritance in part at least world-wide. It is interesting to note here that although their tastes, their prejudices, and their family traditions, not to mention logic and reflection, inclined these men of science to the extreme nationalistic factions, in applying methods and technique and even in using their apparatus they found themselves tempted twenty times a day to abandon too narrow a doctrine. That is what I and many of my comrades reflected when, during a single operation, we saw the surgeon appeal, and pay homage, to the genius of twenty different peoples. I made the same reflection when I saw with wonder that a biologist could not take a confident step without calling as witnesses his equals in Japan, in Europe, and in the Americas.

At that time — I speak of the early years of the century — the ideal of a universal civilization, built up by all that which the arts, the sciences, the philosophies, and even the religions had bountifully contributed to it, knew a period of great breadth and of almost insolent vogue. It did not intoxicate young minds only. Under an apparent pessimism, all the realistic and naturalistic literature of France was a pæan in praise of civilization, the redeemer. In that respect, the literature in question showed a blindness and credulity that we should not today pardon in the most hasty of pamphleteers.

As we must admit, the truth is that at the time there was nothing to let us see that even the slightest crack could be started at the center of this solid ideal of civilization. In France, confidence in the enterprises and ambitions of science had that awed and ingenuous character which makes the visitor from Western Europe smile in Soviet Russia. The debate on intelligence carried on by the adversaries and partisans of Bergson remained an airy game, too sparkling to inspire uneasiness. The ideal of a universal civilization that should be integral and at the same time both ethical and scientific, and that should assume both spiritual and temporal progress, was consequently at the height of its fortune when the war attacked it.

After having brought my own individual perplexity face to face with that of a thousand companions whom I almost never chose, and who generally differed from myself in birth, in age, in opinion, and in nationality, I persist in regarding as a phenomenon of capital importance what may be called the divorce that in many minds has taken place between the concept of an essentially moral civilization, fit, according to Humboldt, to 'make people more human,' and the concept of another civilization that is predominantly mechanical, and that may be described as Baconian, since it is wholly based on the applications of the inductive method.

Curtius is too careful an observer to let a fact of such importance completely escape his notice. Yet he seems not to have realized the greatness of the tragedy. Beyond a doubt he wants to dodge the embarrassing question. 'It would be truly unfortunate,' he says, 'if the telephone, wireless telegraphy, and the cinema were to threaten the vital centers of culture.' He does not believe that those who have pointed out the danger have any chance of being listened to, and he declares that 'the idea of civilization is too deeply rooted in French minds for any one to eradicate it.'

Here is error at the critical point. What lunatic, shaken by the great contemporary disturbances, could have formed the wild and extravagant plan of 'eradicating' the idea of civilization?

The men who, struck by the character of the disaster, have applied their powers of reflection to this serious problem have assuredly only one object, and that object is, not to destroy or to slander civilization, but truly to save it by purifying it; that is to say, by defining it.

As a matter of fact, this delimitation, or definition, immediately showed itself difficult.

Whether or not the fact is obvious at first glance, I have devoted a good part of my works to the examination of this problem, and I admit that I do not believe that it is solved. So far as I am concerned, it grows more complex with the years. If any one should try to make a distinction between a material or mechanical civilization on the one hand, and, on the other, a so-called moral, or true, civilization, in which only the works, thoughts, and doctrines incapable of ever betraying the interests of man should be accepted, he would immediately be brought to realize that the basis of that moral civilization would be slight indeed. Like the poisons employed in medicine to alleviate our sufferings, the greater part of the human inventions fit to give us happiness or pleasure, even of the noblest kind, are yet capable, in dishonest or clumsy hands, of being transformed into instruments of suffering and death.

The advocates of disorder always find some tricky way in which to compromise, in their shameless dialectic, La Fontaine, Rembrandt, Beethoven, and even the divine Sebastian Bach. The words of the most venerable sages are never so jejune and shallow that some one cannot draw from them many contradictory meanings, at least one of which will suddenly show itself to be venomous. If art and philosophy so easily allow themselves to be twisted from their correct sense in order to supply rogues with arguments and arms, is it necessary to turn once again to the inventions of scientific genius, the treason of which has only the other day been so tragically revealed?

Well, yes! At this point in a discussion of which I give a greatly abridged account, minds hesitate and divide. Some, unwittingly following the example of Curtius, lay it down as a principle that civilization is imperishable and indestructible; that if the temporal were to menace the spiritual, 'it would be truly sad,' too sad indeed to be probable, and that consequently it is enough not to interfere with events, for then things will cure themselves.

Others take refuge in despair, which is a 'refuge' in no sense whatever. And I admit that this fundamental despair is sometimes quite devoid of symptoms. I know persons who eat, drink, sleep, interest themselves in various tasks, take their pleasure moderately or immoderately, and in a word live without succeeding in allaying the heavy and inevitable despair that infects and distorts all their thought, all their joy, and even all their sorrow.

I have not yet surrendered to that despair. And if, weak as I am, I am obliged to let events take their course, certain that things will not necessarily end in curing themselves, I want at least to know whither I am being dragged. I do not surrender my right to investigation, knowledge, and conjecture.

Not content with a relative civilization — that is, good in proportion as we make none but a good use of it — I do not give up the idea of defining a moral civilization, a really pure, or, to use a better word, absolute, civilization. And I admit further that science is capable of enriching that most precious treasure. When Charles Nicolle proved that typhus fever, transmitted by disgusting parasites, came as the chastisement of wars and of great disorders, and called man back to a sense of his dignity, he made one of those discoveries which cannot be armed and turned against the species. Moreover, the genius of evil is yet, and long bids fair to be, embarrassed in its undertakings; for example, in the actual state of scientific knowledge it seems difficult, not to say impossible, to create epidemics at will and to propagate them. This impotence of man in certain circumstances to smirch his finest creations is an element of confidence, doubtless slight, but not absolutely negligible. We must make fire of the smallest twig.

But to return: if we cannot hope, we can at least know. There should be no vain recriminations, and no prophetic dreams. I do not much care for the game of anticipation. Humanity still remains so various that it simultaneously offers pictures of an almost paleontological past and living images of the future. Whoever travels in space travels also in history.

An enthusiastic respect for the word 'future,' and for all that it conceals, is to be ranked among the most ingenuous ideologies of the nineteenth century. Scarcely recovered from that intoxication, the people do not willingly believe that the future may not be the home of every kind of perfection, and of every sort of prosperity. Consequently, we shall for a long time see in provincial towns the Hardware of the Future display its sign not far, doubtless, from the Dyehouse of Progress.

That the future has on its side the great strength and the great virtue of not yet existing shall not prevent me from watching it come and judging it impartially.

On certain journeys we are ill at ease because we feel even farther astray in time than in space. The past disconcerts us less than the future; the adult inhabitant of Western Europe who is normal and educated, finds himself more at home among the troglodytes of Matmata than he does in certain streets in Chicago.

As yet no nation has thrown itself into the excesses of industrial civilization more deliberately than America. If you were to picture the stages of that civilization as a series of experiments made by some malign genie on laboratory animals, North America would immediately appear to you as the most scientifically poisoned of them all. For such an experiment America is an excellent subject; so favorable indeed that no one could imagine a better, for there you find an aggregate of human elements, free of tradition, of monuments, of a history, and with no other ties than their redoubtable selves, whose common achievement has begun to reward them.

It seems as if every nation and every civilization had delegated some of its members to help build up this confused, mixed people, upon whom the most extravagant and disquieting experiments are being pursued.

But no one can any longer doubt that their civilization is nevertheless able to conquer the Old World and has begun to do so. America, then, represents for us the Future. At this stage of the discussion, let every one of us in Western Europe loyally recognize whatever taint of America he finds in his house, or in his clothing, or in his soul.

Our future! Before twenty years have passed we shall be able to find all the stigmata of this devouring civilization on all the members of Europe. For a handful of men who view the phenomenon with distrust and sadness, there are thousands who hail it with loud shouts.

America is not, as some persons like to say, a young country in every respect. In material civilization, the American people are older than we, a people prematurely old perhaps, who never properly matured, but who even now are enacting for us many scenes of our future life. It is not, then, uninteresting prudently to observe the actions and reactions of a human group in the grasp of diseases with which we are ourselves threatened.

The sorcerer's apprentice has started the water-spreading mop: the flood is rising on every side, and the apprentice does not know the magic word that controls the terrifying servant.

. . . .

Yielding to custom, I often use the term, 'America' without qualification. Of course, I refer to the United States. I am not considering Central and South America, and Canada, which have not yet been seduced.

It is plain that in my remarks and in my portrayals I have in view, not the American people among whom I have found many excellent friends, and who can present to history some fine portraits of leaders, but American civilization. Moreover, my arrows, passing through America, will hit the whole world, which takes it for a model and admittedly admires it. I have given my life to the eulogy of peace. And with the thought of peace still in my mind, I admit my anxiety.

Must I add that my health is excellent, that my temperament is equable and cheerful, and that I am never bored? I am proud to think myself happy. If I reproach life with its injustice, it is, so far, on account of others. My worldly interests are modest, and are not threatened by the evils that I am studying. The judgments that I form on the progress and aims of the world bear no mark of passion if it be not the passion that I consecrate to the triumph of mind.

GEORGES DUHAMEL

CONTENTS

AMERICA THE MENACE

I

APPROACHING THE WORLD OF THE FUTURE

AFTER supper, the captain and I went down into the cabin, in which the first mate had set up a small wireless set, to chat about life at sea. Between two stories, the officer tuned in and handed us the earphones. 'Still Europe,' said he, 'still the Morocco station.' And across an enormous stretch of white-capped space we heard some scraps of 'Carmen' and the eructations of a gentleman who was reading a lecture on the breeding of Bresse poultry.

Three days after we had touched land for the last time at the Canaries, the voices of the Old World became inaudible. For fifty or sixty hours there was complete silence, so far at least as the mate's toy was concerned, but above, in the room of the Marconi operator, you could hear, day and night, the crackling conversation of the ships that were crossing the Atlantic.

At last, one evening, the captain handed me the earphones. 'Here you are,' said he. 'Here's your America!' I heard plaintive, almost funereal melodies. 'They are hymns,' said the officer, 'sung by Negro choruses. There's never anything else but them or jazz. Every hour now you will be more and more aware of America.'

Four days later, we entered the Straits of Florida, and struggled against the Gulf Stream. Now and then, out to sea, we caught glimpses of the Bahama Islands, which belong to Great Britain — a line of cocoanut palms actually springing from the coral itself, a solitary lighthouse, and, farther away, a lugubrious pile hidden like an asylum for lepers in the solitude of the sea — the immense square hotel to which the Americans flock to drink genuine grain alcohol without fear and without restraint.

The waters of the Atlantic were of a turbid blue, for they were milky with plankton, and made sluggish by the millions of larvæ that the current was carrying north, and that, quickly dying with cold, would soon be food for the fish on the Grand Banks.

'Here,' said the captain as he faced that steaming sea, 'here is the central-heating plant of Western Europe.' And he added with a shake of his head, 'If Europe does not behave well, America will perhaps close the Florida Straits and divert the Gulf Stream from its course. Then Europe will at once become a cold country

— a possibility that may well recall it to a sense of obedience and modesty.'

'Ah,' said I, laughing, 'if the United States plays us any such trick as that, we will dig a tunnel under the Atlantic and send it a bouquet.'

'But,' said the captain, 'it's no joking matter. French chaff won't pass on this side of the world. The specialists say that closing the Straits would be no greater job than piercing the Isthmus of Panama.'

'Ah,' said I again, 'and are there really Americans who take that fantastic scheme seriously?'

'What makes the strength and greatness of America,' murmured the captain, 'is that there are always Americans who think seriously about everything.'

The next morning, in an atmosphere like that of a steam laundry, we sighted Havana.

'Here,' said the captain, 'the hand of America is already omnipotent. This evening we must clear the ship for fumigation.'

'What fumigation, ye gods?'

'The fumigation with prussic acid required of every ship that has taken on passengers at the Canary Islands, and that is later to touch at a United States port. The performance takes place here, in this gateway to America, far from the city, of course, in the open roadstead. We cannot draw up to the wharf until we have had a thorough cleaning.'

The ship began to empty itself of people. Only the captain and two or three men to do the rough work were to remain on board. After twenty days at sea, you saw emerge faces that you did not know — faces of the old and of the sick. Then followed the deck hands and the lower deck — the stokers, blinking like night-birds, the pasty-faced cooks with their swollen legs, and the legion of stewards, who in their shore clothes could no longer be distinguished from the fashionable first-class passengers. The whole crowd was ferried, in absurd little tenders, to the shore, which seemed drunk with Klaxons. Then to the deserted ship came the lighters of the Health Service, with their stinking boilers, their hose, their stills, and their poisons.

The same evening we received a long questionnaire that we were ordered to fill out and sign, and that demanded a swarm of important declarations with respect to religion, political beliefs, private life, marriage, the extent of our financial resources, and the constitutional or contagious diseases with which we might be afflicted.

Seeing me fold up this paper, big as the mainsail of a brigantine, the ship's doctor, a Cantalian whose eyes gleamed with cynical mischief, burst out laughing.

'Now,' said he, 'you're caught. Under penalty of committing what they call here the crime of perjury, and of being punished accordingly, bear in mind that you have put into writing that you are not a polygamist, that you nurse no violent designs against the great North American Republic, that you are neither deformed nor mutilated. As to your diseases...'

He laughed again, coughed, cleared his throat, and went on, more seriously:

'As to the diseases the introduction of which into American territory is strictly forbidden by law, the list is long, tricky, and can be made to apply even to persons affected with extreme ugliness, and to all other undesirable people — an arrangement that is not without cleverness, and that gives to the sanitary inspectors an almost unlimited license.'

'Fortunately,' said I, 'we are done with all such bothers.'

'Oh, no, you aren't!' he exclaimed. 'Summon your patience. You're only at the beginning of them.'

'Really? And what more do they expect of me? At the American Consulate in France I have already solemnly declared in writing that I am not an immigrant, and that I intend to make only a very short stay in the United States. I have produced letters and documents that establish beyond question that I have been invited here by reputable American societies, and that I have not idly undertaken this journey. In order to set foot in this Paradise I have made more calls and gone to more trouble than would be required to get into revolutionary and bureaucratic Russia. I have encountered and braved more suspicion than I had to face in the ports of Turkey at a time of diplomatic tension. I thought that the quality of my passport...'

The doctor shrugged his shoulders. 'We are not on a North Atlantic liner, where matters are arranged with some semblance of decency. But we'll talk of all that later.'

Crossing the Gulf of Mexico took two days, one of which the officers used to purify the ship — I mean to purify it of alcohol. The captain was one of those intelligent men who respect the law so that they may be freer to smile at it.

'When we enter American waters,' said he, 'which are more extensive than any others — when we enter these difficult waters, wine disappears from the table and liquor from the bar. Meanwhile, in order to keep the crew from any temptation to break the law, these gentlemen and I are going to inspect the ship. That is no small job.'

Our talk was interrupted by the loud lamentations of a passenger. He was a handsome old man with refined, regular features and abundant gray hair. We knew that he filled the important position of Dean in an Eastern university. Like most educated Americans whom I have had the honor to meet, he protested against prohibition. He protested in his own fashion, by absorbing every quarter of an hour big glasses of whiskey laced with brandy. From time to time he used to come and favor me with learned and involved discourses: he left me only to indulge himself in solitary dances, in which he imitated sometimes the Russian *trepak* and sometimes the movements of the panther. He had caught what the captain had said, and was afraid that he was going to be condemned to a premature abstinence. Having reassured him and sent him back to his experimenting, the officers, with overalls and lanterns, began a minute search of the ship.

The morning of the second day, feeling the motion of the boat lessen, I realized that we were entering the mouth of the Mississippi. The light of dawn soon revealed to me the melancholy landscape of the delta. I went on deck at once, the better to admire the great stream of yellow water. We steamed up the river for several hours. At last we began to see the columns of smoke and the buildings of New Orleans. Just before you reach the city the river makes a wide bend, and there ships anchor to be inspected by the police and the sanitary officers. We had to wait with what patience we could for almost three hours by the clock before the officers assigned to these different duties condescended to stir. At last, the doctor appeared.

He was a young physician in military uniform, booted and equipped as if for a colonial expedition. He ordered all the passengers without exception — there were approximately a hundred — to range themselves in line on the promenade deck.

He then marched up to us, followed by an orderly who carried a block of wood in which had been bored a large number of little holes. From each of the holes the doctor drew a thermometer. With stiff, precise, automatic movements, he went down the line putting a thermometer into the mouth of each passenger in turn. Soon the whole company of us looked as if we were smoking cigarettes. That done, he strode quickly back to the first patient. Then he began to draw out the thermometers, which he carefully examined and then plunged into an antiseptic solution.

When, not without some cutting remarks, that operation was ended, the officer went again to the head of the line, and placing himself in front of each passenger in turn, with his index finger pulled down the lower lid to examine the appearance and color of the conjunctiva.

That astonishing spectacle reminded me of the opening of *Morticoles*, and I expected to receive willy-nilly some painful injection of vaccine, when the doctor, once more confronting me, tried to slip his finger under my glasses. I do not much care to have a gentleman, even though he has the appropriate diploma, finger any part of me after he has manipulated some dozens of my fellow beings. I briefly told him that I was myself a doctor, that I had neither trachoma nor any kind of conjunctivitis, and that I regarded his examination as superfluous. With an irritated gesture like that of a priest put out in the accomplishment of some rite, and not without hesitation, he turned to the next man.

'Have you,' the purser said to me when I was permitted again to walk the deck, 'filled out and signed the form about what you intend to declare to the customs officers?'

'But,' said I, 'I have nothing worth declaring.'

'Don't be in a hurry to say that,' replied the purser. 'Before you do, read carefully the list of articles or materials, the importation of which is forbidden. The United States protects everything that it manufactures now, everything that it will manufacture in the future, and everything that it might manufacture if it ever took the notion. You smile? You make a mistake. Would you like an example? The American customs bear hard on harpsichords, which they don't make here, but which they probably will make soon. Doubtless they will also take it into their heads to manufacture antiques. Before you land in the New World, be careful to say to yourself that in material affairs this country disposes of a power that seems never to be weakened by a doubt. The United States supplies fresh fruit to the whole world, with the result that our trees at home are discouraged. Before ten years America will have hit on a way to send us roses. My dear sir, read your list and sign — that is, take your oath.'

'But,' said I, 'in the course of a passably wandering life, this is the first time I have ever made a written declaration for the customs.'

'Well, it can't be helped. Unless the traveler is preceded by an enormous reputation, either as a pugilist or as a buffoon, he must arm himself with patience when he enters the United States, especially at one of the minor ports. But never mind! You will be recompensed for these trifling bothers by the affability and hospitality of your American hosts. The cordiality of the citizens will yet make you forget the brutality of the officials. But look! People are hailing you from the wharf.'

Indeed, friends were eagerly waving to me. However, two hours passed in administrative fuss before word was given that we were free at last to rejoin our baggage on the wharf.

'Apparently that's over,' said I to the ship's doctor as I shook hands with him.

'It's about over, so far as entering the country is concerned,' said he. 'But you've still got to leave it. America is the only country in the world that before letting the traveler leave requires him to sign a declaration specifying what profits he may have made during his stay on its soil. Does that set you thinking?'

'Yes,' I replied. 'And the first thing that occurs to me is that the foreigners who land in France at our old port of Havre are dismissed with every attention to their train in five minutes. It occurs to me, too, that before the War I traveled over half of Europe with nothing to identify me except an old visiting card. It occurs to me...'

The doctor genially shrugged his shoulders.

II

CONVERSATION WITH PARKER P. PITKIN ON THE CONQUESTS OF SCIENCE

Parker P. Pitkin himself selected our bill of fare. After an oyster stew in which floated a big lump of butter, and after chops with mint jelly, my companion consulted the menu.

'You'd better take this oatmeal and cream,' said he. 'It will give you two hundred more calories than the sweet potatoes.'

'It will give me *what?*'

Pitkin turned upon me his steady, candid gaze. 'I said two hundred calories. It's much richer in nourishment than the other. You have been traveling; you are tired...'

'Ah,' said I, 'your American humor is delightful.'

Pitkin flushed slightly. 'I'm not joking,' said he. 'Look at the card. Opposite the name of each dish is printed the number of calories that it contains. These bills of fare are arranged by a very competent food-expert. Aren't you hungry any longer?'

'Yes — no — perhaps — I'm sure I don't know. I declare, my dear Pitkin, the word "calorie" contains nothing to frighten me. I have lived much in laboratories, but I think that laboratories and private life are two separate things; the idea of eating calories spoils my appetite.'

He looked at me for a long moment, and then burst into a laugh. 'How fussy you are!' he said finally.

'Well,' said I, 'I don't make any more fuss than your fellow citizens, although I make it in a different way. Your faith in science doesn't bring you tranquillity: it merely gives your uneasiness a different twist. As a matter of fact, you do not feel any better protected than the lowest savage. Moreover, you all have your fetishes. I have just been riding in a Pullman car opposite a robust and healthy-looking gentleman. He had been sleeping for an hour when a man in a neighboring chair began to cough. The robust gentleman was apparently seized with fright. Grabbing his valise and drawing from it an immense and complicated contraption, he carefully sprayed his nose and throat. Finally, putting the apparatus away, he said to me with a smile that "it is better to take precautions." Exceptional though this lunatic was, he gave me a rather disturbing picture of what we are coming to.'

'Don't you take any hygienic precautions?'

'Yes; a few, a reasonable number, but above all...'

'Above all?'

'I don't take them too seriously.'

'You are very wrong. Are you afraid of being laughed at?'

'No, not at all. I'm afraid of turning an imaginary danger into a real one.'

'Are you superstitious?'

'I'm not superstitious, or cowardly, or credulous.'

Parker P. Pitkin is an intelligent and highly cultivated man. For a moment he rested on me his gray-blue eyes, and said with a touch of reproach, 'Not superstitious or credulous? Skeptical, then?'

'Nor am I skeptical, my dear Pitkin. I am a thorough Frenchman. As such, I believe in things enough to be their master, and not enough to be their slave.'

Pitkin blinked. 'He who consents is not a slave.'

'Doubtless, but I fear that you consent with culpable readiness. Do you know that before I was allowed to set foot on American soil, I had to undergo various medical examinations?'

My interlocutor laughed long and loud.

'But,' said I, 'to hear you any one would think that the whole thing were a great joke.'

'No,' said Pitkin, between two fits of hilarity, 'it's serious enough, but it's such a trifle. Don't nurse a grudge about it. It's no great affliction.'

'I go even farther. I'm quite willing to believe that it is not without usefulness. And yet, regarding it as a symptom, I see something in it that is important and menacing. My friend, Dr. C——, wanted to send some patients to the United States. His correspondent demanded by return mail a mass of information about these young people; among other things, he wanted to know the count of the red and white corpuscles in their blood.'

'Don't you think that that was a wise precaution?'

'Just a moment, dear Mr. Pitkin. The question merits careful consideration. You know as well as I that travelers who are preparing to disembark at United States ports are required to declare the maladies from which they may be suffering.'

'Yes. That's the way in which a prudent nation protects its citizens.'

'Very good. As a declaration, no matter how sincere, is not the same as a laboratory report, I can see that before long your sanitary police will require of every traveler a certificate showing that his reaction to the Bordet-Wassermann test is completely negative.'

'Ah,' exclaimed Pitkin, 'what an excellent idea!'

'Of course, that certificate will not be supplied by any physician of the country the travelers come from; he might be suspected of too much good nature. Undoubtedly it will be supplied at the port of embarkation by consular institutes manned exclusively by American scientists.'

'As a matter of fact,' said Parker Pitkin with a slight flush, 'our scientists are highly competent.'

'I don't doubt it. Since syphilis, alas, is not the only thing to be considered, it will be advisable to require of the traveler a good X-ray picture of his chest, and various certificates declaring him free of tuberculosis.'

'Certainly,' exclaimed Pitkin, after a moment's thought. 'Certainly those are vexatious exactions, but the individual cannot complain, since ultimately he is bound to benefit by them. Haven't you been vaccinated against smallpox?'

'Never fear; I've been vaccinated.'

'Do you think the measure superfluous?'

'No, my dear Pitkin. And that is exactly what puzzles me. It's beyond question that, thanks to vaccination, smallpox has almost wholly disappeared from the world. There exist perhaps a hundred contagious diseases. The day when we have an effective vaccine, the use of which is compulsory, against each one of those scourges, we shall suffer no more from sickness, but we shall suffer from the strait-jacket of the law, we shall suffer from our very health.'

Pitkin frowned. 'Your reasoning,' said he, 'seems to me incorrect.'

'I'm not reasoning. I'm grumbling. That's not the same thing. For several days now, I've been thinking that the face of reason might become odious to me. The experience is painful, and excites in my mind an odd resentment. But to go back to the point under discussion. That today international life is complicated by inventions of a new barbarity is obvious to every one. That we see rising in every direction barriers that annoy respectable people, but do not stop the rogues, you cannot dispute. That the astonishing facilities offered by science to the traveler are thwarted by the dictator who speaks in the name of that same science, is something that does not admit of doubt. Finally, that national life, far from being embellished and made secure, will very soon be corrupted by the vexatious folly and vanity of the laws, is what is menacing the entire world, and is what will be borne in upon the traveler on American soil, so long regarded as the land of independence. The prohibition law...'

'Ah,' said Pitkin, wriggling in his chair — 'Ah, you too! To hear you Frenchmen, that law represents the essential spirit of America.'

'I am afraid, my dear friend, that it represents not only the spirit of America, but the spirit of our future world. I know that you are a good citizen...'

'I am,' Pitkin exclaimed proudly. 'As you know, that law is irksome to me sometimes, but I am thankful to the State for protecting me, if necessary, even from myself.'

'That,' said I, 'is nobly spoken. You are weak, and you know yourself to be so. That the State should solicitously concern itself in keeping you from falling into temptation, is a proposition that you loyally accept.'

'As you yourself accept, I think, seeing the State regulate the sale of opium, morphine, and cocaine. Alcohol is just as dangerous a poison.'

'Quite so. And if I use alcohol in a way to ruin my health and that of my children, I quite understand that the State should enter its veto.'

'I am glad to hear you say so.'

'My assent goes much farther than you think.

The State prevents my drinking? Nothing could be wiser, or more just. Very well, then, the State should not hesitate to advance still farther along so good a path. Suppose that I confessed to you that I was sexually intemperate?'

Parker P. Pitkin blushed violently, and turned his head a little aside. 'Oh,' said he, 'that part of your life is no concern of the State's.'

'No concern of the State's, you say? I should like to know *why* it is none of its concern. What! Through certain abuses I run the risk, not only of injuring a health for which I am responsible to my country as a whole, but also of endangering the health of all my descendants! I am a good citizen. I demand that the State protect me against myself, and that, having kept me from drinking, it shall keep me from unseasonable love-making.'

'You're joking,' said Pitkin gravely, 'but it is not impossible that certain declarations...'

'Not impossible? Nothing is impossible! The cohabitation of husband and wife still awaits regulation. Observe, moreover, my dear Pitkin, that the greater part of our fellows are unfit for harmonious and rational fecundation. Almost all of them suffer from some defect, either physical or moral, that they ought to report, so that it may be eliminated. Have you not in certain

States instituted surgical sterilization of the criminal and the insane?'

'That is true,' said Pitkin. 'And that procedure is irreproachable from the moral point of view. As to sterilizing the ordinary citizen who lacks physical or spiritual integrity... Let's not carry anything too far.'

'I do not ask so much as that. I propose that persons whom you have forbidden to drink, and whom, thank God, you will soon forbid to smoke, shall through a skilful superintendence of their home life be prevented from procreating a miserable progeny.'

'The method of superintendence,' said Pitkin calmly, 'must be found first.'

'Oh,' said I, 'that is not what bothers me. In my capacity as the man of action that I feel myself becoming, I am rather considering the way to discover and bring into use a perfectly rational and controlled process of fecundation. What should you say, my friend, to a scientific institute capable of distributing 'selected' semen? We should then have the most useful guaranties. And what an admirable choice we should have to offer to the ladies — the businessman type, of course of the most modern kind; the pugilist type; the sportsman type; the intellectual type; the...'

'Not too many types,' said Pitkin, suddenly serious, 'if you wish to keep down the cost price.'

'Very well! Two types at most, as in the case of apples and pears. To meet the demands of nature there remains to be considered the delicate question of pleasure. Some ingenious mechanism...'

Parker P. Pitkin became interested; he drew a notebook from his pocket.

'Oh,' said he, 'so far as the mechanical part is concerned, the problem is already solved.'

And straightway he made a sketch.

III

CINEMATOGRAPHIC INTERLUDE
OR
THE AMUSEMENTS OF A FREE CITIZEN

'WE'RE going where all those lights are,' said Pitkin. 'It's a movie theater.'

Then, lifting his eyes to heaven, he murmured: 'It's a really splendid theater — one of the biggest in the world. You'll see.'

He spoke with pretended nonchalance. I saw clearly that he was feeling important; the fact that the movie theater was rich and 'really splendid' made him feel a sort of personal pride. Intelligent and cultivated as Pitkin is, he is proud to belong to a country able to build such notable theaters as the one we were to see.

'It's Sunday,' said he. 'Our seats will cost a dollar apiece. The people standing in line here all pay a dollar. The movies are democratic.'

It is true. The people all pay a high price for their favorite pleasure. Jammed together along the side of the building, under a thin rain mingled with fine flakes of soot, they pay dear, too, for the right to wait to be admitted into the temple of the moving pictures.

As there was a crowd, and as we did not give up our intention of going in, we were obliged to take our place in the queue. The people who formed it rarely spoke. Already halfway to the hypnotic condition soon to seize them in the enchanted gloom of the theater, they waited, dull-eyed and patient. From time to time the low doors of the building seemed to swallow a considerable section of the queue. It formed again, added new links, and lengthened.

Another swallow, and we were in the throat of the monster. There the pilgrim gave up his *obolus*, his dollar. There ushers in princely livery divided the crowd, and pushed it through large sluiceways toward the Gargantuan maw. We hurried across spacious and deserted foyers. The floor was deadened with imitations of thick Oriental rugs. On the walls there were pictures that I recognized as copies of copies of famous, and hideous, pictures. On pedestals there were a multitude of statues in some plastic and translucent material that seemed intended to remind one of Greek sculpture, and that were ingeniously illuminated with lamps placed inside them.

'It's rich,' said Mr. Pitkin, tentatively, in case I admired my surroundings.

And indeed the place had the luxury of some

big, bourgeois brothel — an industrialized luxury, made by soulless machines for a crowd whose own soul seems to be disappearing, and looking like a uniform, since you find it in all establishments of the kind from one end of the Union to the other. But let us not lose ourselves in vain reflections. Once again we were pushed forward, like lambs going to slaughter, between two cords that served as handrails. We formed a new queue, endured a new wait in the œsophagus of the monster. Every five minutes the doors opened, and in a burst of music and of night released fifty or so young men who seemed to be under the influence of an anæsthetic, and to leave their pleasure as they are wont to leave a restaurant or an office; that is, with gloomy indifference. As the glutted were immediately replaced by an equal number of the hungry, the theater remained full. A few minutes passed, our turn came, and we were pushed into the abyss of oblivion.

We found still more ropes, still more barriers, still more haughty ushers who guided us toward our places as soldiers guide recruits before the examining board. We had to endure another preliminary pause, while we waited for seats to be vacated. However, we were inside the temple and could see the pictures. They went sliding by somewhere yonder, jostling one another and shimmering like the sheet-lightning of a distant storm. They seemed very near. No doubt they were telling something — a story of which we knew nothing as yet, and which could not at once take hold of us. The crowd round us in the darkness was still, as if asleep. From time to time it laughed, and then we realized that it was very large. Good Frenchman that I am, I waited for my seat, expecting it as my right, before giving my attention to the show. But Pitkin was already taking an interest in the pictures. He was trying to recognize the faces suspended beyond us there in the night. Pitkin is used to the 'movies.' First of all, he guesses that the story was nearing its close. Hearing the beginning after having heard the end is the new way of reading, and of living. It does not embarrass American emotion. Why should it! The show revolves like humanity, like the stars! You take it where you happen to find it. You wait for a complete revolution, and then you leave, glutted. You have had your dollar's worth. Very sensibly you retire.

At last! After a brief pushing and shoving, we found ourselves seated. The seats were excellent. They exemplified American comfort — an affair of relaxed muscles and soft contacts, a comfort of the body and not of the mind.

If I glanced away from the picture for a moment, and lifted my eyes to the ceiling, I saw a sky in which stars twinkled and across which floated light clouds. Of course it was an imitation sky, with imitation clouds, and imitation stars. The sight gave you an imitation sense of freshness. For in that place, everything was imitation. The life of the figures on the screen was imitation, and so was the sort of music with which we were swamped by Heaven knows what torrential and mechanical apparatus. And who was to know whether that human multitude that seemed to dream what it saw, and that sometimes stirred unconsciously like a man asleep, was not imitation also. Everything was false. The world was false. I myself was perhaps no longer anything but a simulacrum of a man, an imitation Duhamel...

For the officer of the guard to have struck this free peasant is an intolerable outrage.

I was still sensible of all my members, but I began to lose any sense of having a soul. It was exactly like being at the dentist's. The seat of my soul became hard and painfully alien. Could it be that they were going to pull out my soul just as at the dentist's...?

Let the young peasant revolt! He is quite right. Let

him flee his unworthy country; let him imitate his elder brothers, and in his turn embark for free America...

My thoughts were no longer under my own control. The moving pictures usurped the place of my own ideas. The music... yes, the music. What was it? You heard it without listening to it. It flowed by like the invisible wind. 'Come,' I thought, 'assert yourself. I will,' I cried in imagination, 'I will, I *will* listen to this music instead of merely hearing it.'

I knew it: it was imitation music, canned music. It came from the slaughter-house of music, as the breakfast sausages came from the slaughter-house of swine. Yes, somewhere out there in the center of the country there was an immense building of black brick — straddled or split in two by the arches of an 'elevated' — where they slaughtered music. Its throat was cut by Negroes as the throats of hogs are cut in the Middle West. It was felled by tired brutes who were half asleep. It was dismembered, it was salted, it was peppered, it was cooked. The result was what are known as 'disks.' It was music in tins.

Listen, listen!—I had just recognized—what, ye gods! The slimy torrent carried down so many things! I felt that I must pull myself together, that I had to be calm! I shut my eyes so as not to see the pictures, so as to listen with all my strength and hear with accuracy. No, I was not yet a helot; I did not belong in that company; I was a free man. I could still do what I willed to do. I still knew what I knew.

This was what I heard: a sort of soft dough of music, nameless and tasteless. It slithered and flowed past me. It was stuffed with familiar fragments, probably chosen for their transient appropriateness to the 'text' of the piece. The engaged pair were, I guessed, about to appear on the screen, for from this musical treacle there suddenly leapt the wedding march from 'Lohengrin' — ten bars only. By what miracle were they suddenly made to merge in Haydn's 'Military Symphony'? Doubtless the reason was that the screen was about to emit a march-past of infantry. I decided to open my eyes and see whether I were right. Cavalry, now! I ought to have known it, though, for here was the first *allegro* of Beethoven's 'Seventh Symphony.' Then came again the stringy connective tissue. And yet... My word: no chance of a mistake! Was it because the lovers were kissing up there that these butchers had dared to slip in four bars of 'Tristan'? The treacle flowed once more. What? But this is dreadful! I recognized the 'Unfinished Symphony,' treasure and victim of the 'movies.' Poor symphony! It had never been worse 'unfinished' than it was here. And now? Jazz already? And was there no one to cry murder? The crowd drowsed, chewed gum, belched, sighed, now and then laughed an abdominal laugh, and digested in the darkness while it contemplated the hysterical pictures. And no one cried murder! For great men *were* being murdered. All those works which from our youth we have stammered with our hearts rather than with our lips, all those sublime songs which at the age of passionate enthusiasms were our daily bread, our study, and our glory, all those thoughts which stood for the flesh and blood of our masters, were dismembered, hacked to pieces, and mutilated. They passed by us now like shameful flotsam and jetsam on this wave of warm melted lard. And there was no one to cry murder! I myself did not cry it; I did not breathe a word. Everything that I loved... The musical tap was turned on.

The tap of the pictures had been turned on too. It spouted up there, or rather, it came to a stop. Two faces, the 'close-up' of which showed the paint, the vaseline, the ugliness, and the dirt, drew slowly together and joined, mouth to mouth. Parker P. Pitkin leaned toward me and murmured in my ear:

'There's a new law; that kind of thing is not permitted to exceed seven feet.'

'What?'

'Kissing on the mouth. The kisses used to last so long that a law was passed. Not more than seven feet.'

'I don't understand.'

'Well, not more than seven feet approximately on the reel, on the film. Even that's a good deal. Think it over.'

I could not think; there was too much noise, too much movement. People entered and left unceasingly. No dreaming was possible. This was not an auditorium: it was a vestibule, a draught, a public square, a hall not only of lost footsteps, but of lost hours, lost hopes, and the final loss of illusions.

The great dramatic 'talkie' was ended. Then came the vaudeville that, throughout the Union, interrupts every two hours the flow of the pictures. Lifted by powerful machinery from a pit in front of the stage an orchestra — a real orchestra, this time — was handed to us as if on a tray. The musicians played in the glare of the crudest and most cruel colors of the spectrum. Sometimes a great organ pealed out as in a church. For the cinema takes the place of everything, provides everything, contains an abridgment of everything. Hardly had the organ stopped when fifty girls, springing forward in the light of a chemical fairyland, kicked up their legs, showing the thighs of modest America bare to the very top. But it was only a glimpse. It was all over in thirty seconds. The 'Follies' succeeded one another in a dizzy jostle. The citizen must not be bored; that is, he must not be roused from his bovine torpor. Twenty seconds finished the live vocalist, whose voice, lost in the enormous structure, soon made you realize the carrying power of 'talkie' speech. Thirty or forty seconds were allotted to young comedians in flaring trousers and short jackets, who raced upon the stage, spouted four jokes and raced off again, and who seemed living symbols of the young American — likable, uneducated, taking what comes, without initiative or individuality — who are mass-produced to stock patterns in 'standard' nights, during lapses from the national Malthusianism.

But there was no chance to reflect. Thirty seconds of musical clowns were followed by ten seconds of acrobats. Hurry, hurry! Faster, faster! There was no pause between one thing and the next, between that next thing and the thing after that! The orchestra was lowered into its cavern, and the screen let through the transient waves of multicolored advertising. Here were the 'talkie' news reels; they recited the latest speech of President Hoover's — an orderly discourse issuing from between full cheeks and accompanied by a hard-working but decidedly photographic smile. Then came the Negro vocalist, who sang for two minutes; too long, a bad break. He gave way to the professor of gymnastics, a sort of serpent-woman who wanted to teach us how to breathe. I wished I could have taught her how to be beautiful! But it was time to wake up — that is, to go to sleep. Here was *the* film. We were going to see the beginning of that precious end. Listen! The music again! Here once more was the musical sewer that bore onward, like so many potato-peelings, the wreckage of our loveliest dreams. And then, the pictures! They went by — it is the only word for it. Although every work of art worthy of the name seeks to remain, they went — the pictures that represent, not life, but a special world, the world of the 'movies,' where everything is false, arbitrary, and absurd; pictures, any one of which, if isolated and immobile, would appear by its scale, its dimensions, its method of presentation, its cheap trickiness, its conventions, its triteness, its accessories, its costumes, and its gestures — would appear, I say, pre-

They follow one another with a feverish speed — so feverish indeed that the public has hardly ever time to understand what is slipped under its nose. Everything is arranged so that, whatever happens, the spectator shall not be bored. He is given no chance to use his intelligence, to discuss, to react, to participate in any manner whatsoever. And this terrible machine, so elaborately dazzling, with its luxury, its music, its human voice, this machine for stupefying and destroying the mind, is today among the most astonishing forces in the world.

I assert that any people subjected for half a century to the actual influence of the American 'movie' is on the way to the worst decadence. I assert that a people stupefied by fugitive pleasures that are only skin-deep, and that are obtained without the smallest mental effort, will some day find itself incapable of doing any task that requires sustained resolution, or of advancing even a little through the energy of its thought. I quite understand that the great enterprises of America — the great ships and the big buildings — will be cited against me. They are beside the point. A building rises two or three stories a week. Wagner needed twenty years to put together his Tetralogy, Littré a lifetime to build his dictionary.

No invention ever awakened from the start so general and so keen an interest. The cinema is, I know, in its infancy, but the whole world has surrendered to it. From the beginning, it has inflamed the imagination, gathered enormous capital, won the collaboration of men of science and of crowds, created, employed, and exhausted innumerable, varied, and astonishing talents. It already has its martyrology. It consumes a terrifying amount of energy, courage, and invention. And all for the most derisory result. I would give all the 'movies' in the world — not excluding those which the men in the trade pompously term their 'classics' — for one play of Molière's, for one picture of Rembrandt's, or for a single fugue of Bach's.

The cinema is not yet an art. I greatly fear that it took the wrong path at the start, and that every day it is straying farther and farther from what I regard as art.

Every work that has held a place in my life, every work of art acquaintance with which has helped to make me a man, represents first of all a conquest. I have had to struggle hard to know any one of them, and to deserve it, after a fervent passion. So far, there is no need to study the work of the cinema: it offers itself at once, like a harlot. It subjects our hearts and minds to no tests. It tells us at once all that it knows. It is without mystery, without subtleties, without depth, without reserves. It strives to gratify us to the limit, and procures for us always a painful sensation as of unquenched thirst. In its essence it is motion, but it leaves us dull and motionless, as if paralyzed.

Beethoven, Wagner, Baudelaire, Mallarmé, Giorgione, Vinci — I take six men at random, but there are a hundred — their work is truly art. To understand the achievement of those great artists, to express it, to suck out the essence of it, I have made efforts that lifted me above myself, and that count among the most joyous victories of my life, and I am still making them. The cinema has sometimes diverted me and sometimes moved me: it has never required me to rise superior to myself. It is not an art; it is not art.

I know that many young men, attracted and even fascinated by the cinema, are obscurely aware of its inadequacy, its errors, and its cheapness, and that they are trying to draw it out of its quagmire. I bow my head before their future martyrdom, for the slavery of the cinema is even more grievous and cruel than that of the theater.

In France the intellectuals, and notably, the writers and artists, play a great part in the experiments and the misadventures of this variety of still-born art. With us the cinema had its beginnings at a time when the romantic tradition still ruled that society of arts and letters which it would be an abuse of words to call in all circumstances the world of thought. However absurd romantic doctrine may have been, it still had a certain nobility. The artist thought of himself as having serious duties and high responsibilities. He arrogated to himself the privilege of passing judgment on the pleasures of the crowd, of condemning them sometimes and, in the name of intelligence, of subjecting them always to severe criticism. Such an artist had his joy, his felicity, his heaven. He was proud, and he wished to be pure. Men have laughed a great deal at that attitude of his. So much the worse for them.

At a certain moment, a number of intellectuals, tired of being bored stiff in their ivory tower, shamelessly sought their recreation in the common amusements of that mob and of those middle-classes whom they had so severely censured. They discovered that, for vacant minds, the café-concert and the cinema were after all not without merit. For some time they spited their stomachs; then, growing bolder and more assured, they bravely surrendered their leisure to diversions, not shameful, certainly, but sterile and vulgar. As they had to save their faces, they shortly began to publish their opinion that the cinema is an art, since great artists, illustrious artists, found pleasure in it. The result was the stupid and sycophantic writing that fills so large a place in the reviews and in the newspapers. A concurrent result was to quiet the conscience of that increasing public of the half-educated who only await a word, a gesture, an excuse, to surrender shamelessly to their appetites.

No true art has ever been a popular craze. The intellectuals who frequent and patronize the cinema ask of it unworthy recreation, and watch it sink into the worst stupidity with admirable indifference. They have allowed a ridiculous language that flouts good sense and harmony to be born and to propagate. They have accepted, without bursting with laughter, such words as 'footage' and the verb 'to feature,' the inventors of which, in a wisely administered republic, would earn a flogging. What is still more serious, they have calmly allowed the cinema, that great gobbler of music, to dismember and degrade for its preposterous entertainments the works of the masters, works hitherto beloved by the elect, and respected, perforce, by the multitude who did not know them.

Thanks to these intellectuals, a remarkable parasitic growth of literature done into pictures has swarmed about the edges of the cinema; to our astonishment we find, for example, 'Le Rouge et le Noir,' 'inspired' by Stendhal. How long will it be before we have 'Britannicus,' in prose and in ten reels, 'after Racine'?

They — but who, good heavens, are *they*? perhaps all of us — have allowed the cinema to become a most powerful instrument for enforcing a uniform standard, alike in ethics, politics, and æsthetics. They have allowed the tidal wave of Hollywood to smother our whole country with its froth, and to choke forever the springs of an old and noble spiritual life.

'Are you tired?' murmured Mr. Pitkin. 'Your eyes are shut?'

'No,' said I. 'Not tired, not the least in the world. On the contrary, I am wide awake, hot, furious, cut to the heart. Let's get out, shall we?'

'Wait a minute,' murmured Pitkin, looking hurt. 'Wait at least for the music. They're going to play something French. Debussy, I think. They are wonderful disks.'

'My dear Pitkin, excuse me. I don't care a rap for the music. That thing of Debussy's? I'll rattle it out this evening on your piano, and I'll explain what it is...'

'What!' cried Pitkin. 'The disks are made exclusively by eminent artists. They are perfection.'

'Pitkin, I don't give a damn for perfection this evening.'

'What! You! You don't want perfection any more? You would rather have mistakes?'

'A hundred times. *Yes!* A live mistake would be better than any of this dead perfection.'

'Hush,' said Pitkin. 'Let us go, then, since you prefer it.'

And we left, annoying a whole row of spectators, thirty persons who were dimly enjoying themselves as if under the empire of some secret vice, and who had long since forgotten what it means to take an active part in anything.

IV

A SHORT DIALOGUE ON THE SENTIMENT OF LIBERTY

'My dear Monsieur Duhamel, what do you think of us Americans?'

'My dear Mr. Pitkin, when any one, between the first and second mouthful, asked my father what he thought of a dish, he used to reply, "I'll tell you my opinion after luncheon."'

'I quite understand, but your first impression is precisely what interests me. What do you think of us Americans?'

'Forgive me, Mr. Pitkin. I don't think of them at all. I haven't seen them yet.'

'What! You've been here a good many days now, and you say you haven't...'

'No. I can't see the Americans for America.'

'Oh, that's one of your French formulas.'

'I can't express myself in any other way, my dear Pitkin. The ant-heap keeps me from seeing the ants: that's exactly what I have the honor of telling you. Between the American citizen and me there rises I know not what monstrous phantom, a collection of laws, institutions, prejudices, and even myths, a social machine without an equal in the world, and with no analogue in history. I see a system rather than a people. Men, about whom I always feel an eager curiosity, in this country seem to me like pure ideograms, like the signs of an abstract, algebraic, and yet already fabulous civilization. You find it hard to follow me. Let me use a clearer figure. If we were in Paris and were walking in the Rue de la Santé, should I have to tell you that the prison kept me from seeing the prisoners?'

'What an odd figure to use in speaking of free America!'

'Mr. Pitkin, America, obviously, has the gift of discerning in the press of ideas and of phenomena everything that is capable of development, of increase, of success — in a word, the future. What you call free America gives me the means of judging what is likely to become of liberty in a future world, and in a society from which I can, without much regret, imagine myself excluded.'

Mr. Pitkin is not one of those Americans who take Constantinople for one of the most curious cities of France, and the Piræus for a man. He is well read, he is intelligent, he thinks for himself, and his opinions are well considered and firmly based. He has visited Europe. He smiled on hearing my remarks, and lifted his hands to Heaven.

'Can you,' he cried, 'criticize our free republic when you live in a divided Europe, where seven nations at least endure a government of force, and when after many unfortunate experiences, your own country is threatened with political dictatorship?'

'Mr. Pitkin, political dictatorship is assuredly odious, and, of course, would appear intolerable to me; but, strange as it may seem to you, I admit that it does not hold any great place among my fears. Political subjection is always violent and crude; it calls for rioting, and ends in provoking it. The spirit of political rebellion is not extinct in the heart of man — fortunately. The Soviet and the Fascist dictator — to cite only those two — call forth, not only in their own country, but in the whole world, a too ardent protest for any philosopher to feel greatly discouraged on account of them. When men have reached a certain degree of culture, and have become conscious of their capacities and of their hopes, they grow restless under the restrictions placed on them by a national tyrant or by foreign domination. On the other hand, they adapt themselves easily enough to another kind of dictation, that of counterfeit civilization. That is what makes me anxious.'

Mr. Pitkin blinked and shook his head in disagreement. 'I do not fully understand you,' he said. 'Our political system is far from perfect, but...'

'I repeat, my dear Pitkin, the political problem does not greatly interest me. It is variable, fugitive, always provisional. Although you do not think yourself the slave of a political or social system — which to my eyes shows a charming complaisance on your part — you are the slaves of your moralists, your lawyers, your hygienists, your doctors, your city planners, even your teachers of æsthetics, to say nothing of your police, your publicists — how many more are there? In short, you are the slaves of America, as, following your example, the whole world will some day be the slave of itself.'

Mr. Pitkin's forehead showed quite new lines. 'It seems to me,' he remarked, shaking his head, 'that you keep harping with a strange insistence on a single problem. I don't understand any too well...'

'For men like me that problem is undoubtedly the most important of all. No, you *don't* understand me any too well. The fact is, that your enslavement is, you might say, imperceptible.'

'If it is imperceptible,' murmured Mr. Pitkin,

with an uneasy smile, 'don't force me to perceive it.'

'Wise words, my dear Mr. Pitkin. But haven't I already said too much? This slavery has established itself so stealthily and advanced with such caution that men could hardly keep from accommodating themselves to it. The restraints imposed on the individual in the name of the obviously reasonable principles of hygiene, morality, æsthetics, and social safety — in a word, of civilization, *our* civilization — rouse little resentment in the modern world. At the start they give the citizen a sense of security that should compensate him for certain small sacrifices. They establish themselves insidiously; they quickly assume the character and strength of organic habits. In the modern state most men good-humoredly recognize their incompetence in a multitude of things, and modestly delegate every power to specialists whose zeal is all the greater because it rarely goes unpaid. Nations, so slow to stir when it is a question of recognizing and helping genius, accept without too much protest a great many measures that are presented to them as proper to facilitate the functioning of the social organism.'

'Oh,' said Mr. Pitkin, 'you're the sort of man who nurses a grudge. You're still thinking of the thermometer that they stuck into your mouth — you, a doctor!'

'Put that out of your head, my dear Pitkin, I have forgotten the thermometer. If a people brings to the task of protecting itself some small measure of impoliteness, of barbarity, of simple-mindedness, or of stupidity — why, that's merely natural, and pardonable. No: I am thinking of the spiritual life of the nation. The citizen, I tell you, subject to so much supervision and investigation, to so many inquisitions and censorships, is not merely the prey of the bureaucrats; he himself accepts the task of helping his tormentors and of doing a large part of their work. With respect to every act of his life, he is obliged to answer interrogatories, to fill in returns, to gather documents, to offer up a tribute of waste paper to the monster. He passes a good part of his life in 'declaring' something or other, under penalty of law. However strong in him is the spirit of discipline, a time comes when he regards himself less as protected than as enslaved, and finds that the whole pleasantness of life has a tang of bitterness and mockery. Political régimes pass, Mr. Pitkin, but this fearful idea of civilization does not cease to expand and to prosper. I have still to find...'

I had been speaking eagerly and now stopped

short, not because I was out of arguments, but because I was out of breath.

'You seem to be on the point,' cried Pitkin, 'of admitting that all these things are not peculiar to America, since the whole world is affected with the same disease.'

'At this moment, my dear Pitkin, America is forcing men to revise a great many of their ideas and standards. It's a merit, I agree. America seems bound to lead the rest of humanity along the path of the worst experiments. Today, America affords us a measure of how complete the effacement of the individual — his abnegation and his annihilation — can become.'

Mr. Pitkin shook his head obstinately. 'Liberty, as I believe you have already said, lies, not in institutions, but in the sensation of freedom that we derive from them. We are the freest people on earth.'

'I know. But wait a moment. I have in my pocket several of your small coins on which is stamped the word "liberty." And what do you see immediately under that word? The figure of a buffalo or an Indian. Oh, irony! They represent two free and spirited races that you have destroyed in less than three centuries. Moreover, my dear sir, these reflections of a foreigner find something to feed on in the very writings of your most illustrious fellow-citizens. I do not speak of your poets, who almost all turn away in bitterness from their native land; I do not speak of your publicists; I do not speak of a Mencken who inveighs each day against the American because he takes a sort of inverted patriotic delight in doing so, and because he who loveth, chasteneth; I speak of your social philosophers and statesmen, who study the march of your civilization, and who do not dissemble their distress. I have jotted down in my notebooks certain phrases of Mr. Hughes that will perhaps astonish you. "Liberty," says that wise man, "has need of safeguards and of protection against organized pressure and against bureaucracy, so that the citadels of individual liberty need not surrender. Our institutions were not created in order to bring about uniformity of opinion. If that were so, we should have to abandon all hope.' I do not cite these phrases as models of eloquence. Such as they are, however, they say something forcible and terrifying. Admit, my dear Pitkin, that the brilliant civilization of which America is the protagonist, the herald, and the prophet, seems to be leading us toward one of those periods which figure as dreary gaps in the history of mind, toward one of those periods where the dearest desire of a

scandal is not what you think. Every citizen shall be a member of the league who will willingly do each day some act of non-conformity, no matter how unimportant — for example: darn his own socks, refuse to go up in an elevator, but ask for the stairs, deny himself the cinema, refuse to buy an automobile on credit, refuse any brand of soap the manufacturer of which declares he spends two million a year in advertising, promenade the streets familiarly with a Negro friend, decline to utter the word "standard," offer his seat to an old woman, smile, sing, go for a walk without any definite object — and so on and so forth.'

'But, Monsieur Duhamel, you can't be serious.'

'The second league! Listen: we will form a league to increase and encourage disobedience to ridiculous or oppressive laws.'

'Alas,' said Mr. Pitkin, 'the desire to disobey has made great progress since prohibition.'

'In that case, Mr. Pitkin, hurrah for prohibition! But let me go on. The third league will have as its object to learn how to do nothing.'

'What do you mean?'

'By doing nothing, I mean stopping to think a little now and then.'

'Unquestionably, you're joking,' said Parker

P. Pitkin. 'You'll never make any one here listen to proposals like those. Come. We've talked a long while; let us have some refreshment. Should you like a glass of root beer? It's made out of roots, and *as* beer it's laughable. A thousand apologies, but I can offer only what I have.'

'My dear Pitkin, let's let the leagues go. What must be found, in the interests, first of America and then of the whole world, is the hidden underlying reason of the disease.'

'What evil are you talking about? The disease that has overtaken liberty? Don't worry about it so much. Do as we do, and everything will settle itself. How do you like our non-alcoholic drinks?'

'Vile, my dear Pitkin. I regret to say it. They are absolutely bad, and of no social efficacy. Remember; the Soviet Republic has kept alcohol. The act is one of Machiavellian cleverness. Not in a glass of root beer can an uneasy citizen forget his cares. In fact, prohibition may perhaps be the salvation of America, but not in the way you think.'

V

ALCOHOLIC BEVERAGES

OR

A DISPUTE ON THE FUNCTIONS OF THE STATE

'GREAT heavens, my dear Mr. Pitkin, is it a murder, or are they rehearsing some horrible scene for the movies?'

Ten paces away, a door had opened. A huge man had appeared, who, with the most contemptuous indifference, was dragging by the leg a human scarecrow that he proceeded to dump on the sidewalk. Already the door had closed and the giant disappeared.

'Let us hurry,' said I, 'and help this unfortunate creature.'

'Don't stir a step,' said Mr. Pitkin, clutching me by the arm. 'It's a drunk. Much better leave him to settle with the special police without any help from us.'

While my host dragged me away I turned two or three times and looked back. The poor devil looked like a young man of the middle classes. Like every one else in this country, he wore a respectable ready-made suit, upon which he had vomited. His heavy breathing sounded like a death-rattle.

We went on for some paces in silence. Not for a long time had it been given me to see so dreary an example of drunkenness. I gave myself up to meditation on the disadvantages of alcoholic beverages — a meditation interrupted, however, by new incidents. We met two gentlemen supporting — indeed, almost carrying — a companion whose feet barely brushed the ground. Was it a marionette, a lay figure? No! In a face that in color was like the white of an egg two doleful eyes, focused on infinity, were becoming glazed. From a mouth that hung open like the mouth of a man who has been hanged, and that was swimming in saliva, came a hideous groaning.

'Ah,' said I, 'if he weren't groaning, you'd take him for a corpse.'

'Another drunk,' said Mr. Pitkin, with a pretense of pity.

'It's a holiday here, then?'

'No. It happens every day, I must admit. This poor young fellow is trying to prove, in the only way he knows, that he has money, that he is in a position to spend a great many dollars. Perhaps he'll die, perhaps he'll go blind. That depends on what poison was in his drink.'

'Mr. Pitkin?'

'Monsieur Duhamel?'

'Do you know that I feel myself slowly becoming a prohibitionist?'

'Don't joke about so sad a thing.'

'Believe me, I'm not joking. I am disgusted and revolted. In my own country I have not seen for ten years a single case of drunkenness that has so distressed and even angered me as this one has. I know that in France we have a most blameworthy tenderness for the man who is drunk, for Silenus, even for the sot — at least so long as he is jovial. But at home we do not often see that besotted, tragic, deadly drunkenness which seems so generally prized in your country. Do you know that about twelve o'clock the other evening I went into the wash-room of the Pullman I was in, and what do you think I found there? Two gentlemen in their shirt sleeves, face to face, standing erect in spite of the motion of the train and of their own uncertain equilibrium. Each had in his hand one of the paper cups provided for drinking ice water. They were filling themselves bumpers of some sort of foul rum that they drank one after the other without uttering a word. They looked at me with unseeing eyes. They finished the bottle and went staggering off to roll into their berths. Do you know, Mr. Pitkin, that the other day

I dined on an English ship? Your police, who were guarding the wharf, smelled of bad brandy twenty yards away. They stood there like phantoms, phantoms of the law. You could have tumbled them to the ground with a push of your finger or even with a breath. Do you know that in all the clubs to which delightful friends have invited me they wanted me to drink cocktails of eau de Cologne, of dentifrice, wood-alcohol, paregoric, of varnish, of chloride of soda, and of vitriol? Do you know — and how can you help knowing? — that the society men whom I meet are all more or less distillers? They pass a part of their time in their bathrooms mixing infernal compounds with which they hope to experiment on my highly vulnerable person. Do you know that yesterday evening I dined with a consul, and that I drank real wine? Felicitate me, Mr. Pitkin! "This wine," my host told me, "reached me escorted by six policemen armed with rifles and automatic revolvers. For in this country men would resort to violence to get a little wine." Do you know that all your immense population is obsessed, that it thinks of nothing except alcohol, alcohol, alcohol?'

'Eh,' said Mr. Pitkin, 'you don't have to tell me that! But we're out of luck tonight. Here's still another of those wretched drunks.'

We were in a public park intersected by roads along which automobiles were tearing. A big young man was walking across the grass. He wore a handsome overcoat, but he had shed his walking stick and his hat. He came on like a mechanical toy that is out of order. He could not see; he hit the low branches of a spruce tree and fell to the ground. He got up, drifted away, and fell full length into a clump of rose-bushes. Again he rose and began groping his way toward the murderous road.

He did not look like a drunken man; rather he looked like an animal in a laboratory, a part of whose brain has been removed. By some miracle he reached the edge of the sidewalk, and with deep concern I saw him dash toward the stream of automobiles.

'Hurry, Mr. Pitkin! We can't let him be crushed to death.'

Once more Mr. Pitkin seized me by the sleeve. A car stopped. Two brawny fellows got out, took the drunkard fairly into their arms, and lifted him into the automobile. He was saved, but I was still moved, still angry.

'You've got to admit,' I growled, 'that these drugs are frightful.'

'Agreed,' Mr. Pitkin sighed. 'Furthermore, we have to realize that the American does not know how to drink. He always looks as if he were committing suicide.'

'Alas,' said I, in disgust. 'I begin to wonder whether after all prohibition isn't necessary.'

The placid, good-tempered Pitkin stopped in his tracks. He stamped his foot; he grew red in the face; he stuttered. He seemed on the point of getting angry. 'Don't talk to me of that abominable law!' he cried.

'What! my dear Pitkin, what! Abominable law? You have often praised it when I found fault with it. Now today, when I am on the point of approving it, are you going to attack it?'

'You can't understand,' groaned Mr. Pitkin in a choked voice, 'the seriousness of the problems that this law presents to us.'

'It seems to me that, as a matter of fact, the prohibition question goes to the very center of the American soul. You haven't always agreed.'

'That's the fact,' said Mr. Pitkin. 'I am a good citizen. I dislike to disavow the laws of my country, especially before a foreigner. But — well — you've seen too much. But please remember that you haven't seen America when it had alcohol...'

'Can it have been worse?

'It was something different, undoubtedly, and it wasn't pretty either. Moreover, we again have alcohol — an alcohol more poisonous than before, and in addition we have this law that throws everything into confusion, complicates everything, and corrupts everything. To have sober working men, to suppress the crazy-drunk Negro, to preserve the purchasing power of the multitude for American industry and commerce — admit, Monsieur Duhamel, that that may pass for wise politics. Well, it isn't! You'd think that the Devil was in it. I say the Devil himself, and not merely the hundreds of thousands of bootleggers who make their living from contraband liquor, who are going to vote for Hoover, and many of whom are as rich and powerful as kings. What you call, correctly enough perhaps, our hygienic and moral dictatorship has, like all dictatorships, produced among us an ignoble spirit of spying and discord. It has stirred up every kind of base passion in the crowd. You see that people drink; it is only too obvious. The middle classes are killing themselves. They are rich and can afford every kind of murderous liquor. Our young girls, whose nice manners you admire, absorb enormous doses of poison. The present members of the middle classes will be quickly worn out. Others will succeed them. The man of the people waits his turn to get access to the cocktail, and to absorb his skinful of adulter-

legislatures a series of questions that hitherto man debated either with himself in his secret soul, or with his God.'

Mr. Pitkin stopped on the edge of the sidewalk and grasped a button of my overcoat.

'Ah,' I said to him, 'that is a gesture that you Americans have not made for more than two hundred years, but that you still can often see under the trees of our small country towns.'

'The truth is,' he replied, 'that your remark bothers me greatly and makes me examine my conscience. In a word, you accuse the American Government of substituting itself for God. That certainly is a serious matter. But if God... loses his grip? I'm not speaking for myself. The Pitkins, father and son, have always been Methodists and reasonably religious, if you don't object to such pragmatic language. So, let me repeat, I do not speak for myself; I speak rather for the crowd of men who have lost hold of religious principles. What are we to do, then, if God goes out of sight?'

'Well, let man fight it out with his own conscience, so far as certain problems are concerned.'

'And if man has no conscience? Then it's highly necessary that the State...'

'There you go again. You're falling back once more on this accursed prohibition. Mr. Pitkin, if the State interferes in the spiritual life of man, we shall quickly be in a mess; we shall attain nothing but disorder and absurdity.'

My companion shook his head, and for a long time we walked on in silence. Finally, by a violent contraction of mysterious muscles, Mr. Pitkin began to waggle his ears like a worried animal.

'After all,' said he, 'matters will perhaps settle themselves if we have good, honest alcohol, as they have everywhere else.'

'My dear sir, you remind me of that Norman mother who said to her son as she walked with him to the train, the first day of the War, "I have two pieces of advice to give you. First, don't drink any bad liquor, and second, if there's any fighting up there, you keep out of it."'

'You're joking, Monsieur Duhamel. Just the same, I know what I want to say. Everything will be less serious if we have pure alcohol, and if we can be free to make a moderate use of it.'

'Bravo! And in spite of everything call it prohibition. You're a genius!'

'Alas, no! I'm no genius. But at home I have something truly remarkable — a small bottle of real French brandy. I brought it back from France after no end of trouble. I have kept it two years. We'll open it this evening in your honor.'

'And we will ask its advice, my dear Mr. Pitkin.'

VI

THE AUTOMOBILE
OR
THE LAW OF THE JUNGLE

THE handsome red apples that the Negroes polish by first spitting on them and then rubbing them hard with a cotton rag; the pears, as uniform as a patent medicine — the pears that, like juicy grapeshot, America sends in salvos to the ends of the earth, for I have eaten them even in Egypt — I can guess where they are grown, and I even know where they are sold. But the legs, the lovely legs with their beautiful contours, obviously mass-produced, that are sheathed in glistening, artificial silk, and that the little knickers clasp with so charming a garter — where are they grown? The knickers — yes — a thousand pardons! I speak only of what I see, of what indeed every one sees. How do the American ladies all manage to procure those same delectable legs which they display so generously?

Thus wandered my vagrant thoughts while I risked my life in the automobile of Mrs. Graziella Lytton.

The car glided along a cement road divided in the middle by a wide band of white. A hundred feet ahead of us was another automobile and a hundred feet behind us was still another — and so on, both ahead and behind, to infinity. We were deep in the country. Such is the modern solitude.

Every ten miles we saw at the edge of the road a pile of scrap-iron more or less eaten by rust. It was the carcass of an automobile. To the scorched skeleton there still adhered shreds of imitation leather or velvet that the sun, the rain, and the vermin had almost destroyed. The dead car disturbed no one. It might rot there in peace. No one looked at it; no one dreamed of breaking it up and taking it away. As for those who once occupied it, they had been taken to a hospital long ago. Or, if unharmed, they had picked up their suitcase, climbed into a hired car, and left the useless wreck at the side of the road. The cars that pass the corpse never stop to smell it, as dogs do among themselves. They have the sublime indifference of flies in the presence of a dead fly. An insect civilization!

From time to time Mrs. Lytton made a sketchy gesture by way of explaining something to me, and whenever she did so, the car took a large and negligent lurch. With her little shoes of imitation crocodile playing on the pedals; with her skirt driven back to the middle of her thighs by the combined effect of the movements she made in driving the car and of the breezes; with her hand resting on the steering wheel, the little finger in the air as if she were drinking a cup of tea, she was wonderfully graceful, distinguished, and, despite her forty years, deliciously girlish, and 'photogenic.' Above all, photogenic. She was the modern goddess, published in an edition of two or three million copies, through the services of a vigilant industry, as the prize and the pride of the American citizen.

'My dear Mrs. Lytton,' I said at length, 'you are obviously a skillful driver, but aren't you going a bit fast?'

She laughed — a clear, full, symmetrical, well-modulated laugh, the identical laugh of the blonde stars who live on the screen, the laugh that the 'talkies' will soon reproduce for our ears, and that we shall recognize as an old acquaintance. She laughed, and lightly pressed the accelerator.

'Have you never had an accident?'

Mrs. Lytton laughed heartily. 'Oh,' she said, 'you know we have many automobile accidents over here.'

'Yes,' said I, 'yes, I know. I have been in

America only a fortnight, and I have already found myself in three collisions. That's not doing so badly. The day I landed, I saw a woman run over. Look out, my dear lady, it seems to me that just now...'

'That's nothing. A bad turn. Think! Two hundred and fifty thousand accidents a year, and fifty thousand fatal. Of course every one has to take his share. I have done my bit — but nothing except Negroes.'

'What, my dear lady, you have run down Negroes?'

'Not many. Only two.'

'And they're dead?'

'You can't kill Negroes so easily as all that. Their skulls are too hard.'

'Really?'

'Oh, they lack presence of mind, whether on the road or at the steering wheel. You know the saying: "In case of accident, the Negro lets go the wheel and raises his arms to heaven."'

'Yes, I know. And women shut their eyes.'

Mrs. Lytton unsheathed that film-star's laugh again. I sent a smile toward the back seat. There sat Mr. Lytton, an athletic and profoundly silent gentleman, who was smoking a cigarette — like the criminal just before his execution.

'And Mr. Lytton,' said I, politely, 'doesn't he drive?'

Mrs. Lytton let out a tiny globule of a laugh — like the sound a bottle makes as you finish filling it. 'Oh,' said she, 'Mr. Lytton hasn't the time. He's too devoted to his business.'

Mr. Lytton lowered his eyes almost imperceptibly. It was nothing, and yet it was enough to make me understand that he drove very well, but that he did not like 'scenes.'

In spite of myself, I turned my gaze back to the road that perhaps we were to leave the next moment, once and for all, for that green embankment and the future world.

'And if,' I said, 'you happen to have some slight hitch, some insignificant trifle like a flat tire — you are, I suppose, an excellent mechanic?'

'I?' said Mrs. Lytton disdainfully. 'I? I know nothing about such things. If I puncture a tire and Mr. Lytton isn't in the car, I stop at the edge of the road and wait. I'm a woman, you see. The first gentleman who passes — there, that man who is coming along behind us, for instance — will be only too glad...'

She laughed again. This lady knew only one kind of laugh, but she brought it off successfully every time. She laughed, and stirred up the machine again with her foot. Since her youth she had made these big gulpers of gasoline roar along every road. In this country automobile maturity legally arrives at the age of sixteen. And at that infantile age, rouged and powdered young girls pilot mastodons to and from school.

A brief silence followed that was barely disturbed by the hum of the six cylinders. We were really in the country, yet the free wind of the prairies smelled of cheap gasoline. Were we really in the country? If so, where was it? The road was bordered with big hoardings, not presenting a flat surface or even painted in such a way as to create an illusion of reality, but complicated with depth and perspective; that is, made like a stage-setting with converging wings, and with figures cut from wood in the open space between, and at nightfall the whole thing was illuminated with rows of electric lights at top and bottom. Behind these enormous structures there may perhaps have been what passes for the country hereabouts.

Ah, here were the outskirts of a small town. While still some distance away, you saw its ugly, cheap little houses, and dominating everything else the single building that serves in this landscape as a sort of equivalent for our church spires. But — but — what was this hideous sight?

It was an extensive marsh full of old automobiles — broken, worn out, gaping at the joints, wrecked. There were hundreds of them, of every kind and make. They had been brought here like old 'plugs' turned out to grass, whose hide and guts are not worth taking to market.

They had been dumped into the ditch in a cloud of dust. It was the charnel-house of automobiles, the graveyard of scrap-iron. Yes, over yonder, there are old, poor countries where the people pick up old chair-springs and iron slop-pails in order to resell them to the junk man, who takes them to the iron-works, where they go again into the melting pot. What ridiculous economy! How odd! How amusing! Here, we were in rich America, where they wear out many automobiles in order to manufacture and sell many more. We were in the great country that does not produce in order to enjoy in moderation and in reason, but that enjoys as it acquires — feverishly and without sense — so that it may be able to produce a little bit more.

The small town was left behind. I do not know its name, its history, or its beauties. Has it some beauty? Has it even a history? As to its name, we may assume that it is modestly content to call itself, say, Athens, Paris, or Rome.

My eyes, tired of the hoardings with their

advertisements, turned to the interior of the car, and I suddenly saw in it a symbol of the world of the future. What better symbol of it could there be than this madly rushing machine, turned loose at full speed between two pasteboard landscapes, steered by a charming woman with manicured nails and beautiful legs, who smoked a cigarette while traveling between fifty and sixty miles an hour, while her husband, seated on the cushions of the rear seat, with a set jaw scribbled figures on the back of an envelope.

In the Southern States I was shown some acres of virgin forest. They were carefully enclosed within a barbed-wire fence. They belonged to watchful owners who were protecting a bit of solitude against the civilizing furies as you guard some precious object in a glass case. The jungle itself, bitten into on every side, retires, loses foothold, leaves this worldly scene, but the spirit of the jungle is immortal; frank and unashamed, it still lives along the highways.

Men, always on their guard against one another, deteriorated as a result of that self-constraint infected with hypocrisy which we call politeness. Carefully masked, and kept under control, their faults and vices did not have free play, except in close intimacy. Prejudices relating to morals and manners held educated people in check. The struggle for life, for the best place, and for the biggest share, preserved a veiled and subterranean character. The hierarchy of the intelligence still struggled to make a place for itself. In certain circles, even money suffered a sort of discredit.

The automobile came and changed all that. It has made every affectation disappear. It has torn off the masks and restored the free play of the natural passions to the post of honor. It has put every one back into his place. It has restored the reign of force. And what force, I ask you? The force of money, the single force that, after all, counts, and can triumph.

The man whom his most indulgent friends regard as a sot, whom his wife despises, to whom no one would trust the least important piece of business, who is incapable of carrying his own suitcase, who has no sense, no skill, to whom almost no one listens when he speaks, whom no one could read if he wrote, who has neither moral energy nor any true courage, who has no authority, no power of command — that man enters his automobile; what a superb revenge for the vain and the inefficient! He who would not dare to impose his will upon a horse knows that he can demand anything of a machine. Let's see, what does the machine weigh? Two or three tons, perhaps? Very well, then, reflect a moment. I press my foot on this small pedal and I can lift the two or three tons to the top of a mountain at the speed of an express train. I turn to the right, I turn to the left. Can I stop? I stop when I please, and I start when I will. I am a very powerful, intelligent, and skillful person. Here is the highway; that is, the jungle. Make way for money! I know the rules. They are simple: I pass every one who is not so rich as I; I let myself be passed by those who are richer than I. Nothing could be clearer.

'We have made every imaginable effort,' a manufacturer of automobiles one day said to me with a faint smile, 'to put this astonishing implement indiscriminately into the hands of any man who comes along, for the ordinary man is our best customer. The man who is good for nothing else is still good enough to drive a car.'

These business men, who are also psychologists, have succeeded far beyond their hopes. The whole success of the automobile lies in putting an enormous material power into the hands of men who often merit no power of any kind, and who never would have any without this miraculous mechanism.

The effect of this wide distribution of power

is worthy of admiration. The automobile is a lever that increases all our vices, and that does not exalt our virtues. The automobile sends rushing up from the depths of our being all sorts of curious traits that, generally speaking, are not to our credit. It reveals and emphasizes the least noble lineaments of our natures. It makes a sensitive man irritable, an irritable one insane. It makes a strong man a brute, it makes a brute a beast. It offers chances beyond the reach of imagination for churlishness, for perfidy, for cowardice. It sets problems for our virtue that seem insoluble, for, in France at least, experience and law have made them forever perplexing. Shall I take into my car that old woman with the heavy bundle? Oh, yes, of course — so that in case of accident she may demand a fortune from me! Shall I stop on this deserted road at night near that disabled car, the occupants of which are signaling to me — and fall into the hands of a band of thieves and assassins? No, thank you! Step on the gas! Am I to risk my life to spare this drunkard, this cripple, this sick man? Why should I? The insurance company will pay.

The one true piece of luck in respect to automobiles is that the Other Man's car is also vulnerable. What if he were able to strike us, shove us aside, and sweep us away, without injury to himself!

On, on! Quicker, quicker! At first we thought that the automobile had killed boredom. Nothing kills boredom. If we speed up the car, it is because the way is long and boredom is close at our heels.

To enjoy going slow, we have to know how to go fast; but when we know how to go fast, we never again go slow.

Speed also permits me to avoid the look of those whom I offend, whom I spatter with mud, whom I inconvenience, whom I endanger. They hardly have time to see me. I hardly have time to feel ashamed. The automobile lets me be a cad and a coward with impunity.

May we hope that the traditions of chivalry will be born again on the highway? What a joke! It is on the highway that you learn to judge men — often to despise them, and always to fear them.

Rules, a code, have been established. They are a scorn and a derision! The road is to the swiftest, as the jungle is to the strongest. Like the animals, we seek only one thing: to intimidate the enemy. And the Other Man is the enemy.

They say, 'What sport!' It is the sport of

lazy creatures, a sport which intelligence quickly deserts, and in which the muscles find less and less to exercise them.

What is the difficulty in learning to drive an automobile today compared with the difficulty in learning to play the flute or the violin, even modestly well?

The automobile has not conquered space: it has spoiled it, ruined it. There is no longer any solitude, or any silence, or any place of refuge. He who flees the city in an automobile immediately finds the city again.

But fortunate, most fortunate is the horse! He will suffer no more. The holiday is in his honor. No longer will he fall between the broken shafts; no longer will he shiver on his stiffened feet; no longer will he be made to rise with kicks and blows. The automobile will release him from the need of suffering, and above all of living. The best service that can be done for that good beast is to relieve him of existence. Not-existing is not terrible. It is no-longer-existing that excites our horror.

If the automobile of Mrs. Lytton could have understood my thoughts, it would have bucked furiously and thrown its ungrateful passenger into the ditch. But the automobile of Mrs.

Lytton had the virtues of the machine: it had no scruples, and it nursed no grudges. It kept on. It kept on, indeed, extremely well. Here we were in the great city.

Finally, the car stopped; did it want to punish me after all?

'Let us get out,' said Mrs. Lytton. 'We have to park here, well away from the center of the town where parking is absolutely forbidden.'

'Then,' said I, 'what are we going to do?'

Again, full and clear, came Mrs. Lytton's laugh — the laugh of a movie 'star.'

'If you please,' said she, 'we're going to walk.'

I had not hoped for such luck. Accordingly, we left the machine and penetrated into the heart of the great city where the automobile has killed the automobile. For now, thank God, we know that speed is the one thing that will rid us of speed.

VII

LANDSCAPES

OR

THE IMPOTENCE OF THE PAINTER

COULD I have brought myself to look to my left, I should have seen the profile of Mr. Merriman. The lines of his profile were pure, refined, and intellectual. Unfortunately, I could not bring myself to look to my left, or to my right; like the excellent Mr. Merriman, whose hands grasped the steering wheel, I felt that I had to look straight ahead of me.

Chicago stretches along the shore of Lake Michigan for approximately twenty-eight miles — stretches, or rather did stretch that distance, for, while I am writing my sentence, it has lengthened another mile. Chicago! — the tumor, the cancer, among cities — about which all statistics are out of date when they reach you, and in regard to which every calculation must be done over again, since the figures always change before you finish it!

This urban monster is, nevertheless, but half a city. It radiates from a point on the shore of the lake; its heart is on the border of empty space. It is like half an apple. You are astonished to find so much noise and activity on the edge of nothing. For the lake, which is as big as a sea, is not the sea. It has not the breath, or the tumult, or the life, or the soul of the sea. With its marshy smell, which you meet everywhere, even in the bathroom and in the ice water from the special tap, with its gloomy horizon, and its great, livid, shimmering surface, reflecting a dull sky with slow smoky clouds in it, the color of pewter, it lies there like an enormous piece of absence, like a warning of death, like a symbol of non-existence. Chicago comes howling to a standstill on the edge of eternity. Certain fishing villages are said to lie 'in peril of the waves'; I greet with a solemn hymn Chicago, the proud, lying in peril of nothingness.

Of what use is it in these days to be 'the youngest metropolis in the world'? Hardly risen from the marshes, Chicago already seems old, already too narrow, stifled by its very strength. Though it has only been in existence for a few decades, it already suffers as much as a city that has endured for centuries. It did not foresee the automobile, which stuffs and suffocates it. It has scarcely the years of a grown man, and yet the wave of time has already submerged and condemned it. Some years ago, the city reclaimed from the lake a large strip of land on which now run roads that serve as race-courses for automobiles, roads for which America has borrowed the name of boulevard. Cars are turned loose there like toys that have gone mad. They seem free at last to rush against one another, to defy one another. There are no pedestrians, and no horses. That space they have conquered for themselves — for their very own.

'Here,' muttered Mr. Merriman, 'wheel to wheel, bumper to bumper in a solid block, every one does at least thirty-five miles an hour.'

'Is it against the law to go slower?'

'Oh,' murmured Mr. Merriman, 'imagine a blood corpuscle that let itself go slower than the rest, and loiter along at its own convenience.'

The automobiles formed, indeed, a horizontal cataract — a compact, well-directed flood, the drops of which must not touch one another.

Night fell. A thousand cruel lamps lighted and clashed like so many daggers. I did not see the lake, but I divined its presence on my right — an abyss of silence, an infinity of cotton-wool in which the noise of the demoniac city was lost.

'Wait,' said Mr. Merriman, 'wait. We are still only on the edge of things. You have not yet seen the real face of the city. There is more to Chicago than all this.'

I half closed my eyes, for I wanted to pull myself together and to muster my strength. The high range of buildings with a sky-line that makes you think of a man with some teeth out, I refused to look at, and glimpsed only from the corner of my eye. By an ingenious system of approaches, the automobile returned little by little to more congested regions where the blood of the city became thicker and flowed less rapidly, where the trains of the Elevated roared like iron storms over an unclean and stupid crowd — men, beasts, and machines — and suddenly, without my being able to understand how we got there, we rolled into a large subterranean passage full of light and noise.

'This,' said Mr. Merriman, as if replying to my thought, 'is the lower street. Here, there are two streets, one above the other. The greater number of vehicles pass above us. But this is the more convenient way to go where I'm taking you — that is, to the shore of the river. Here, let's get out. Hurry!'

A short walk brought us to some stone steps on the bank of the Chicago River.

I said to myself, 'I salute thee, ancient river. On thy lone and marshy banks, Cavalier de La Salle camped when, driven by his wandering spirit, he sought the great inland valley. Is it indeed thou, O ancient Indian river, thou whom the white man hath chained, thou whose course he hath altered, thou flowing no longer into Lake Michigan at the will of thine own lazy waters, but changed to a sewer, running, ashamed and enslaved, to the Mississippi that, with other foulness, carries thee on to the shark-haunted Gulf of Mexico?'

Wide, deep, and fetid, the river was at this point a harbor. The two superimposed roads crossed it on a two-story bridge, on which two rivers of men, vehicles, and noise flowed above the river of dirty water.

Dominating the roar of the streets, a new voice spoke suddenly. A steamboat arriving from the lake was demanding passage with long blasts of its siren. Then at the base of the bridges appeared clusters of lights, linked intimately with a coincident medley of noises. Groups of red lights, raised high, blazed from moment to moment with convulsive flames, and each flame was accompanied in perfect time by a harsh, strident ringing, a clattering storm of sound. The flame and the noise were so perfectly mingled that you thought that you heard the light with your ears, and that the sounds dazzled and blinded you.

On that imperious signal, the vehicles stopped

both in the upper and in the lower roadway. A moment later there were two thousand of them, one behind the other, throbbing in a withering stench of burnt oil. The flames leaped, the bells clanged, like shooting pains. The double bridge was empty and deserted. Then in the middle it split transversely. The two halves, carrying their two fragments of street, with their carriage-ways and sidewalks, rose swiftly into the air. They lifted themselves on end, and presently, illumined by the lights below, set two great square shadows see-sawing on the foggy sky. While the great boat, trumpeting like a crazy elephant, advanced between the two stumps of the bridge, other bridges farther on were opening to give her passage. Still farther on, other grouped lights began to vibrate and other sets of bells to light up, and other thousands of automobiles began to tremble with impatience and to stink. And all of it, so far as you could see, was going on at the bottom of a ditch, for the scene was dominated by thirty immoderate buildings that at that hour blazed with every light that pride can invent. Each building was an advertisement: one of a gum manufacturer, one of a famous newspaper, one of a great movie palace, and then there was one that served as a lighthouse for the boats on the lake, and another that bore on its roof a Methodist church complete, with porch, nave, and spire, but, curiously enough, without a cemetery. And from the height of their forty stories the buildings watched the river where the boat glided, grunting, by.

The boat was passing; it had passed. The bridges closed again. The flames died down. The automobiles leaped forward. Where was I? At my feet against the mole, little waves were slapping. The water was dirty, but still it was water; that is, something simple and natural. The murmur of it was closer to my soul that night than all the clamor of the life of man.

'Here,' said Mr. Merriman, 'here is Chicago.'

'Yes,' said I, 'it's Chicago. Ah, if I were an Italian, I should invent Chicaghissimo.'

We laughed a little, a very little. Mr. Merriman is a scholar and a man of letters. He was born in this city. Day by day, he has watched it wax big with unwholesome fat, become delirious, and then insane. He speaks of it with a kind of fright mingled with pride that did not deceive me: I clearly saw that he confused love with astonishment. But did he really confuse them? I hesitate to affirm it. Mr. Merriman earns his living in Chicago. He is saving — I know, for he has told me — that he may buy a little old stone house on the shore of the French Mediterranean, where he can go to pass his vacations and later to die in peace.

Allow me for a moment to digress from this scrappy narrative. Let Chicago stand back for a moment, behind its tainted fogs. As I write these lines, I am in my own home, in my own country, in my garden in Île-de-France, caressed for yet a little time by the smile of a civilization that is ancient, wise, and noble. And yet even here I am harried by crazy visions. There comes to me sometimes again a hideous desire once more to be at the window of the monstrous hotel where a man can change his room every night for seven years without sleeping twice in the same one, to be high up there for yet another moment as on the balcony of death, and to gaze with my whole strength, trying to comprehend this wretched, demented world, this world that has no witness, this hell that lacks a Dante.

O painters, my friends and brothers, you can never make anything of Chicago! You will never paint this world, for it is beyond human grasp. Chicago is no more paintable than the desert. It is prodigious and untamed; it is not a living thing. It has nothing in common with that familiar spirit who had no dearer wish than to find again the features of a face.

Everything that for centuries the artists of old Europe have painted has been in scale with man. True greatness is not a matter of absolute dimension: it is the effect of happy proportion.

America is devoted to its ephemeral works. It erects, not monuments, but merely buildings. Should it fall into ruins tomorrow, we should seek in its ashes in vain for the bronze statuette that is enough to immortalize a little Greek village. Ruins of Chicago! — prodigious heap of iron-work, concrete, and old plaster, the sole beauty of which will be gay plants and moss — I evoke you with horror and weariness of spirit.

The man to whom I said these things is a sculptor. His is an imported talent, for he was born in France. But for a long time his very bones have been infected with the American disease. He listened to me, shaking his head, and all at once exclaimed resentfully: 'I think that sculpture has a great destiny here, in spite of cement, trumpery, and pot-boilers. The country is rich enough to buy marble, if only out of vanity. And then all these buildings call for decoration. I am not talking of the buildings in spurious Gothic. I am talking of the great sincere buildings — rigid, massive, large and high — that after all express America so well, and that, wealth aiding, seem to need to blossom out at the top into statues, *rilievi*, and ornaments. Look at them, those great buildings: they owe it to their pride to be richly decorated. But — think of it! — they give me only three months to execute a group in marble or in granite. For any delay after that, it's a thousand dollars a day forfeit. What artist can accept that bargain, and not become a tradesman? And what artist can live here unless he accepts those terms?'

It is true; the building grows, and keeps growing. It cannot wait for the inspiration of some, or for the leisurely experimenting of others. Too many allied interests demand that it be finished. The artist must fall into step. He must obey; he must either hurry or quit.

The building rises. However simple its lines may be, it is often disfigured with blazing signs that cover or crown with the lettering that remains the parasite of modern architecture. The building rises! It takes on life: twenty elevator shafts pierce it from top to bottom. It is crowded with systems of lighting, power, heat, and cold, with conduits for the telephone, for water and for gas, with ventilating pipes, with chutes for letters, for soiled clothes, and for refuse. It shelters the population of a French prefecture. And the whole of it speaks, eats, works, makes money, speculates in the stock market, smokes, drinks alcohol in secret, dreams, and loves. The building lives! In the evening it is lighted up like a Christmas tree. Flood lights, placed on neighboring structures, inundate it with torrents of light that seem to make it translucent, and that cost a fortune a night. The building lives, but less, I assert, than the little temple of the Wingless Victory, less than the Sanctuary of Medinet Habou, asleep under the Theban dust. The building lives the life of mortal things. It is built for thirty years, perhaps for less. The very men who built it will demolish it tomorrow, and put into its place something else, bigger, more complex, and more expensive. All the ideas that animate it smell of fashion and of death. At the very hour of its building, men are planning the way to tear it down. It has no sense unless it meets the newest requirements. Even if it is not in itself ugly, displeasing, and badly proportioned, it does not for a moment have that flavor of eternity which we always find in a genuine work of art.

Sole interpreter of the genius of America, architecture seems debased in its designs, in its methods, and in its achievements. It does not know the soundest ambition of all: the ambition to defy time.

In that ridiculous moral atmosphere in which

swarms, not a great nation, but a confusion of races, how can one possibly find that sublime serenity which art must have if it is to quicken and flower? I do not view the theories of Taine without suspicion. A *post-hoc* explanation, by a geographical determinism that a wise man would never make a basis for prophecy, is too easy. Yet all the same it is curious to observe that the moral climate of North America imitates in its sharp changes the variable humor of the great valley that extends from Labrador to the Gulf of Mexico. When the wind blows from the south, it is like the breath from a stove. If the wind shifts, it becomes on the same day like a killing blast of winter. Almost all America works in a draught, now burning, now icy. You are forced to conclude that man has adapted himself to it and likes it; at any rate, in the manner in which the Americans heat their houses and their railway trains, they follow the same programme; that is, sudden bursts of heat interspersed with shivering intervals. It is the climate of the 'boom' and the 'crash.' We are far indeed here from Touraine with its smiling horizons, from the moderate Seine and from pure and sonorous Provence.

The American people have raised their inhuman cities on a soil that never invites moderation. Lakes, valleys, rivers, forests, plains — all are huge; nothing seems made to incline man to thoughts of harmony. Everything is too big; everything discourages Apollo and Minerva.

I have gazed on the Father of Waters, the legendary Mississippi. I found it hard to see. The greatest river in the world is very often invisible. It is strangled among the docks of New Orleans; as it will not endure the bridge from which you might at least look at it, it remains hidden, as secret as the Cloaca Maxima. Mile after mile in the plains of Louisiana, where the oil tanks glisten among the fields of sugarcane, I have pursued it. The great river is necessarily invisible: it traverses the dull plain between immense levees, like a shameful prisoner.

I have seen Southern forests that sadly dip their gray, mossy branches into the somnolent waters of the bayous. I have seen millions of birds desert the burning savannahs, and under a wave of smoke, I have seen the boiling of the yellow marsh water. I have seen the Texan prairies parched by the summer sun. I have seen the Negroes picking cotton in Alabama. I have seen the Appalachian Mountains, where you can find a peaceful retreat. By what frightful miracle does this land, which stretches from the tropics to the icebergs, this country, which may be without grace, but yet is not without nobility, find itself so degraded and made ugly? The people who inhabit it seem more anxious to plunder it than to love it and beautify it. These fields are not ugly, but despised, slaughtered, and squalid, for they are left in prey to 'renters' who seek nothing except an ignoble profit. Near the amorphous villages burn mountains of rubbish. The great cities like Chicago and Pittsburgh, in spite of their wealth, live on certain days bowed down under a lid of greasy, pestilential smoke. Seek—and find, as you find in Connecticut, for example—some charming landscapes in which there are water, pasture land, and cliffs, and they will be disfigured with hoardings that display advertisements that fairly scream. Discover in the mountains a green valley traversed by a lively brook, and it will inevitably be encumbered with a steel bridge like a cage, soiled with a funereal whitewash. I understand clearly that a new country cannot provide itself with the little ancient stone bridges that are the pride and treasure of our provinces. But think! Natural riches that are asserted to be inexhaustible, the effort of millions of brave men, administrative ability that we are required to respect, and three centuries of conquest without a halt or retreat, have been able to produce nothing but a churlish civilization, whose hostile ugliness defies description.

North America, which has not inspired painters, which has not raised up any sculptors, which has prompted the song of no musicians, unless it be that of the monotonous Negro, and whose barbarously industrial architecture seems to care not at all for the judgment of future times, has yet produced poets and writers. Almost all of them — oh, mockery! — have turned from their native soil, in bitterness of spirit. I am not speaking of the numberless scribblers whose obscure labors go to feed the thousands of magazines and of daily newspapers as thick as dictionaries. I speak of the clear-eyed men who are striving today to evoke and to judge the mad society in which they grew up, the men whose work expresses now despair, now anguish, now a furious disdain, and now a vengeful irony.

But to paint Chicago? How can one do it with mere words or colors? Music alone, it seems to me, could accomplish the task. And rather than any imitative rhythm, soon lost in this tumult, it should be bitter funereal chords, a heavy prelude to chaos.

VIII

THE KINGDOM OF DEATH

When the wind blows from the southwest, Chicago smells of glue. The breath of the abattoirs flows back toward the heart of the city, and, tenaciously mingled with the atmosphere, with human beings, and with thoughts, seems the natural and intimate odor of American luxury.

The Chicago abattoirs are a city within a city, a world in the bosom of the world, the sanctuary of carnivorous humanity, the realm of scientific death. That realm has its laws, its manners, its customs, its shops, its restaurants, its hotel, its railway, its police, its populace, its crowds, and its princes.

I knew it. I had been told it. I thought of it and tried to imagine it, all the while that the Elevated express was carrying me at full speed into the middle of a taciturn and, as you might say, a sacrificial crowd.

It had been raining ever since morning. The tops of the buildings were covered with clouds. A funereal light filtered down as if through a crêpe veil. Oh, the two daily baths are not an affectation in a land where the sky sheds more soot than light!

The Elevated train slipped through the air on dizzying rails. On our Parisian 'Métro' we place illusory railings that doubtless would not stop the train if it should choose to leave the track. Why should I mind, then, that the train here springs ahead on unguarded rails like shining swords, and that it takes the curves at full speed. When that happened, the crowd swayed as if mowed down. I recovered my balance, and, turning toward my neighbor whom I had jostled, I begged his pardon. He pushed me back and growled between his decayed teeth, 'No one says "pardon" here.'

We left that miserable crowd and entered a different train — the special Elevated train for the abattoirs. The cars were, if possible, rougher and dirtier than those which we had left. They exhaled a sickly, musty smell of phenol and the butcher's shop. They slid with sharp, griding noises toward the land of slaughtered beasts.

Here were the stock-yards, extending as far as you could see. Through the play of a strong and compact organization the animals are brought here from every part of the country — sheep that pastured in the Far West, in Nevada, Wyoming, or Idaho; cattle from Texas and Nebraska; swine from Iowa and Missouri; all the animals for which in France we hypocritically reserve the gentle term 'domestic,' the animals of the house and of the family; and which here are nothing but the raw material for a meat factory. They are pumped, sucked, or drained into the yards by the long trains of the slaughter-house. They arrive and keep arriving every day, and every minute of every day, for if the great machine is to function, if its wheels are never to turn without grist, the river of living flesh must roll on unceasingly, in hurrying waves.

They had waited in the pens, lowing, bleating, or grunting, and pawing with a restless foot the brick or cement floor. Then the buyers came, the mounted buyers who with a long pole touch their chosen victims.

The animals are at once pushed into covered galleries, and, as if they all understood that they can go nowhere else, take their way toward death. They march on slowly, surely, one behind the other, like soldiers in the trenches of a battlefield — a terrifying comparison that suggests itself so strongly that you are forced to accept it. The beasts go forward, they mount upwards. From time to time, they utter a long, uneasy wail that, like many another, is lost in the gray, cottony sky.

The griding Elevated carried us on. We left the poor brutes behind; we should meet them again only too soon.

The story that I wish now to tell has been sticking in my throat for almost a year. It lies like a weight on my chest. It is time to free myself of it. But I don't know by what handle to grasp it. I am afraid of forgetting something, of not ridding myself of it completely.

The stock-pens grew dim in the mist. Here were the buildings of the abattoirs — amorphous, incomprehensible, made, they say, of flotsam and jetsam patched together without a plan, with no apparent design, like some laborious chaos.

They call it 'young' — this America that is always caught unawares by the event. But consider these buildings! Here was not the modern factory such as you like to imagine it. It was a mass of barracks bound together by any sort of makeshift.

It all smoked, panted, and spat. Everything was the color of coal, with huge signs, pipes, footbridges, towers, skeins of cables, lamps burning livid under the light of day, and an unimaginable odor of burning animal waste, of the wash-house and of warm intestines.

Sometimes in the choked streets there appeared a long train of manure that, ringing its bell to clear the way, advanced, reeking. Other trains followed it, whose cars were white, and hermetically sealed. They were the refrigerator-cars, that carry the meat across the continent.

Here, like great fly-traps, were the morose buildings in which the clerks struggle with their mass of papers, like employees of a Ministry of Carnage.

There it was that we left the train. I say 'we' advisedly. Good Dr. Brooke, attentive companion, be sure that I do not forget you!

We found the elevator. Good. Do not forget that American politeness contains three strict rules: place the chair of a lady when she is about to seat herself at the dining-table, leave her the inner side of the sidewalk, and take off your hat when she enters an elevator. We took off our hats, then, without hesitation. These girls, who all resembled the renowned heroines of the 'movies,' were yet not going to dance a 'number' in a 'super-production.' No, they were the stenographers of the establishment, and were going from one story to another to stretch their legs, though they pretended to be busy.

Ah, here was our guide! Though still a young man, he held an important position in the establishment. He had a grave, direct gaze, the air, at once attentive and preoccupied, that the

American business man has imposed like a uniform on all the business men of the world, and that makes you believe that he has great cares, important duties, remarkable projects, and heavy responsibilities.

Mr. Pickleton outlined our itinerary and asked various preliminary questions.

'Monsieur Duhamel is not easily upset?'

'He used to be a doctor. As such he served in the War.'

'Yes — well, you can't tell from that. We'll have luncheon first; it's safer. And we'll begin by taking a turn through the museum.'

The 'museum' is the place in which the by-products are shown. It is as small and coquettish as a glass case in a shop. And, indeed, it is a display of goods. And what goods you see there! Every kind of thing is there: drums, tobacco pipes, buttons and knives, harness and rackets, tooth-brushes and clothes-brushes, shoes and gloves, suits of clothing, drugs, chemical products, toys, and soaps — everything that can be made from horns, hides, bones, and fat, from blood and other fluid substances of the body, and from whatever else remains after the great butchery. 'At Chicago,' says a famous apothegm, 'they use every part of the pig except the squeal.'

I regarded all these exhibits with a complaisant

and inattentive eye. You see, I had not yet caught, understood, and defined their underlying odor.

Once more we were in the street under a drizzling rain that was half water and half dirt. We heard a prodigious clamor that resolved, mixed, and confounded the rumble of machinery, the cries of animals, and the uproar of men. Again there reached us the whiff of the phenol that tried in vain to cover the smell of meat and offal.

We climbed into an automobile, which smelt of stale cigars, and whose cushions, in imitation leather, were stuffed with imitation horsehair, for the by-products are valuable materials, and continued our expedition.

Here was the hotel for the cattlemen, like the manor-houses that you find in rural England. It was roomy and comfortable. Here, the dealers in live-stock come from their distant States to lodge so that they may be at the very center of their field of battle.

Once more we were in the street, once more we entered the automobile. In it we rode to the club where we were to have luncheon. I do not know its real name; I call it the Club of the Big Butchers. The parlors — wadded carpets, heavy velvet, all the crude luxury of an old-fashioned bourgeoisie — were cluttered with statues in bronze and marble of young pigs, horses, cattle, and sheep, the sacred animals of the place. Hung upon the walls were the portraits of the high priests; several generations of the princes of the meat trade, the hereditary masters of this omnipotent porkocracy. Above each portrait there burns unceasingly an electric bulb, like a lamp before an ikon. Thus you can consider with attention and respect the features of these obscure men who are among the mighty ones of the modern world.

The luncheon was served in a great room from which the livid daylight was driven out by glittering light-brackets. I was hungry, and why not? Was I not wont to be hungry when, standing among the wounded and the dead, I drew off my rubber gloves at dawn that I might swallow a bit of boiled beef or a hunk of bread? I was hungry, but with a hunger in which there was no pleasure, and which anything would satisfy. The courses succeeded one another. At length, the colored waiter brought a mysterious dish. He lifted the cover with an obscene smile, the smile of a pander who lauds and promises some ignoble pleasure. He lifted the heavy silver cover and showed us — a piece of meat. He carved it, and with a gluttonous grimace put the slices on our plates. Then he withdrew with a smile, and disappeared on tiptoe.

Well, it was the best piece of meat I ever ate in my life. That is beyond dispute. I ate it; I have eaten it. I was caught. I was an accomplice. Between Chicago and me there was a corpse, the corpse of a steer.

Let the memory of the irreproachable coffee cast a veil over that picture! At once we were on our way! The word was 'hurry, hurry!' for here they make use even of the waste scraps of time, the by-products of your corpses, O minutes of life!

Once again we were in the automobile in the street, in the noise, in the rain, that by-product of an immolated sky, and in the smell, which suddenly rose and grew strong and full like the blast of a siren. Once again we entered the incoherent buildings, and stepped into one of the elevators. Suddenly, behind a red door, we heard the cry of animals.

We entered. The cry made, as it were, a bold leap in intensity. It now filled the universe to its very edge. Could it be that they did not hear it over there, on the other side of the Atlantic? A warm mist clung to my glasses and blinded me. At first I was choked by a strange odor of hot cow-dung. I wiped my glasses and looked round me. We were on one of the footbridges that dominate the scene.

We saw a great hall, full of confusion. At one corner entered the covered passageway through which arrived the stream of hogs. The animals, covered with filth, were lassoed by one hind foot, and suspended from a running chain. They hung head down, and screamed their frightful hymn of death in chorus. But the chain carried them on and brought them at once to the butcher.

The butcher was a brawny Negro. He wore a suit of overalls that was sticky with blood to the arm-holes. In his right hand he held a strong cutlass. He was alone on a platform like an actor. The chain passed in front of him, and the hogs, whose weight made them almost inert, were presented to him at the proper height. Then with a calm, sure gesture, he pierced their necks with his cutlass. There was no hesitation, no violent effort. The steel buried itself without haste. A stream of blood gushed forth that, uniting with other similar streams, flowed along the gutters of the floor and fell to the lower stories, there to be made into I don't know what — foods, drugs, jewels, explosives...

The blood spurted. The animal gave a last gurgling cry. Another cry at once replaced in the chorus that of the singer whose throat had been cut. The animal that had perished was already bobbing up and down in the scalding vat. Imagine a long, fetid vat where the carcasses are freed of their filth. They entered it the color of mud; they came out of it pink, pink forevermore, with that pale and delicate pink to which you would prefer to apply some other adjective than 'tuberculous.'

But we could stay no longer, for the chain was moving on, with its funereal rumblings and arthritic creakings. The scalded swine hung by the tendons of their hind legs, head downward. Their promenade continued. The chain turned back on itself several times in the great hall. Men in couples awaited its passage, silent, tired-looking men, each of whom knew a single gesture. One man singed the carcass in a wide flame of gas. Other men, armed with special knives, scraped each a portion of the skin; as the chain proceeded, they shaved each a square foot of hog — always the same square foot. The same man performs the same action every day of the week. He earns two, or two and a half, dollars a day. So said Mr. Pickleton, adding by way of excuse that it is one of the trades that can be learned in two hours. But the chain was proceeding. A man waited. With a single stroke of his knife, he severed the head, which swung back and forth, held by the skin of the throat. Another man began to divide the carcass in the middle. A third man completed the job. A fourth began the work of disemboweling, and a fifth completed it. The chain proceeded. Experts cast on all this meat a glance long since blunted. The chain kept on. The pallid pink carcasses advanced one after another in procession, all of the same deathly pink. Little by little, the hogs lost every part of their bodies, and when finally the last scrap dropped from the chain sixteen minutes had passed since the Negro butcher made his thrust.

And all the time the scream continued, ever renewed at the start of the chain — that scream, so strong and so alive that the packers will make something of it some day. It is absurd that that enormous sum of energy should thus evaporate and lose itself in space. They will make music of it, pretty tunes for the jazz band.

Come, no reflections. Forward, march! Once more we crossed footbridges, roofs, and terraces. Once more we felt the fine rain of wet cinders. The smell of the swine and their scream pursued us for some time still. At last we came to heavy iron doors, painted a brilliant red like an insistent allusion. We had reached the slaughter-house of cattle. We entered a room on the same level as the ground. It was less noisy than the other. The beasts here were passive; they seemed stricken dumb. They arrived, packed in small wagons. The Negro butchers were walking up and down on a high platform. One of them halted before each wagon and raised above his head a sledge-hammer with a long springy handle. There were five or six cattle in each wagon: five or six blows of the hammer did the work. Sometimes the small pointed end of the sledge missed its mark and sent a broken horn flying. Sometimes a dull lowing rose from the panting mass. The Negro passed on. For a moment the five or six animals remained standing side by side, held upright one by another. Then the wagon tilted, and at one stroke discharged the dying monsters. They were seized by their hind feet and lifted to the endless chain, which carried them to the man who cut their throats. A torrent of blood gushed forth, and there was some convulsive twitching.

Mr. Pickleton pulled me by the sleeve. 'Come, come,' he said, 'we have so many things to see.' In spite of everything I was fascinated by the action of the butchers. I have seen hundreds of men die, but deep in my heart the capacity for horror is not extinct. Death, even when mechanized in this way, even when reduced strictly to the proportions of an industrial process, remains awaited them, a man in cap and workman's blouse, who makes the ritual gesture that is his trade, the essential act of his life. After thirty-two minutes the beast was cut into fragments.

In the sheep-room things moved faster. A procession of animals went stumbling to their death. Again we saw the Negro butcher, the endless chain, and the funereal progress.

We ourselves had to move faster. With a polite but authoritative gesture, Mr. Pickleton urged us on to other sights. Halls, red doors, stairways — we encountered them all again. Sometimes for a moment we got a breath of the outdoor air with its savor of fog, oil, and corruption. From the suffocating steam-room, where quarters of meat danced in the vapor, we passed to the refrigerating-rooms — huge, deserted, deadly halls, through which we passed at a run between two lines of disemboweled cattle, stiff as soldiers on parade.

We reached the workrooms on a lower floor where wholesale cooking is done. A whole population of pork-butchers are needed to mince the pigs' fat. There is another of tripe-men to wash the entrails. Monstrous chopping machines minced mountains of flesh into sausage-meat. You could go in a boat over the sea of warm lard. We were hurried down a story, like the merchandise. There again we found the lard. A machine ejects a pound at a time — a white, warm, revolting jet — into pasteboard containers that another rattling machine makes as if with hands, as fast as they are needed. *Bzit, bzit*, the spitting machine shifted from one carton to another and filled them at a single spurt. The lard hardens at once under the sleepy eyes of girls in white caps. This is the Empire of the Sausage. Evenly and accurately peppered and salted, the meat arrived from the upper stories in conduits. It was there in the pipes, to whose mouths the workman with a rapid gesture, curiously obscene, affixed yards and yards of sausage-skin. When all was ready, they turned the tap that controlled the flow of meat, which, liberated, turned itself into sausages at racing speed. An understrapper received it in long skeins, which dripped here and there, and hung it on metal frames.

It was enough, quite enough. Rather than see more we sought the faithful rain, so subtly permeated with oil. Yes, I know, Mr. Pickleton, I know. I saw, everything was clean — cleaner, I admit, than the slaughter-house and the pork-factory in my village. That the hand of a Negro sometimes goes astray in the machinery and becomes a part of the sausage-meat, as malicious gossip says, is fundamentally of no importance. Everything is sterilized in gigantic boilers. I repeat that it is all clean — clean, and heartbreaking.

We were passing along the street among the smoking buildings where is prepared — at what a price! — the food that we require as carnivorous animals.

Suddenly I grasped Mr. Pickleton's arm and put to him this ridiculous and almost cruel question: 'Do you like it here?'

Mr. Pickleton looked at me, and an imperceptible veil dropped over his fine black eyes. 'I do not live here,' he said.

After a moment he added in a lower tone: 'My family lives out of town. I have a house in the country.'

'But there are tens of thousands of men and women who do live here, who spend their whole existence here?'

Mr. Pickleton gave a helpless shrug of the shoulders, and then, grasping my arm, led me away, for he is a man of action who does not waste his time in vain reflection.

It was seven o'clock in the evening. The Elevated express was crowded. It clattered across the tumultuous city. It was useless to try to arrange my thoughts. I was in the grip of Chicago, as I might have been in that of some fell disease.

In spite of all fatigue, all sorrow, and all anxiety, I have always kept my enjoyment of life as a dear and modest treasure. I am not sure that hereafter I shall not find in all joy an after-taste of the abattoir.

The mine, the iron-works, the paper factory, the abattoir — those are the foundations of the civilization of which we are so proud. If you have not gone down into a mine, if you have not felt the sulphurous breath of the paper factory, if you have never breathed the flat, animal odor of the abattoir, if you have never seen the furnace vomit forth its deluge of delirious metal, you do not know, my friend, all the sadness of the world, or all the dimensions of man.

The Elevated express was full. We were standing side by side, a jumbled herd of passengers. Would a Negro pass along the length of the car and free us from this bestial existence by hitting us a dexterous blow on the forehead with a sledge?

What were these rending screams? More hogs? No, they were the car wheels shrieking as they went round the curves. We were changing our neighborhood, almost our province. Sometimes the car emptied. Through the windows, wet with rain, I watched the crowds patiently waiting before the doors of the 'movie' houses. What was it that the slowly advancing crowd made me think of? Was it not the animals who mounted the incline to the slaughter? I wanted to turn away my eyes. What were these pink forms in line in front of me: were they more pigs, more and more pigs? No. I tried to rally my spirits and more closely to regard the legs of the American ladies, those beautiful legs in flesh-colored stockings. I forced myself not to yield to my obsession, but to gaze at these pretty women of the richest and happiest people on earth. Alas, in spite of their lovely smooth stockings, the women in the Elevated at this hour were employees with tired faces, who, their day's work done, have to spend an hour in an Elevated train in order to reach their lodgings — I dare not say their homes.

Finally, I reached the hotel, my own shelter, my own burrow, my own refuge from this crazy town. At last I should have a bath, and perhaps attain forgetfulness. Well, no! The soap that I grasped smelled strongly of the abattoir. Moreover, it undoubtedly *came* from there. The linen with which I dried myself — with what by-product was it bleached, for it also smelled of the

IX

GAYETY

'Monsieur Duhamel, you look out of spirits.'

'My dear doctor, I am tired. And — why should I conceal it? — I am depressed, dreadfully depressed.'

'Perhaps your hotel is not comfortable enough?'

'Of course you know, doctor, that my hotel is the biggest hotel in the world. There I enjoy what you call comfort; I have a fine bathroom, a tap of ice water, heat, light, a radio on the table by my bed with six feet of cord attached so that I can go and come, shave, write, read, sleep, and still listen. On that same table is a magnificent Bible, the gift of the Gideons, an admirable society of commercial travelers who call themselves by that name, not, as an amateur of polite letters might suppose, because they wish to honor André Gide, but, very modestly, because "Gideon was a man who did exactly what the Lord wished him to do." On the Bible there rests an anthology of poems in the English or the American tongue. Whitman appears in it, among two hundred other gentlemen of less importance. Finally, on the anthology, is a telephone directory in three volumes, for I have a telephone. I can also be accommodated with a typewriter. Oh, my dear doctor, comfort! I have it, it has me, we have each other.'

'Well, Monsieur Duhamel?'

'Well, I have had a bath, the second for the day. And I got out of it as depressed as ever.'

The doctor turned on me a kindly, astonished gaze. 'Dear me,' said he, 'how subtle and complex you Frenchmen are!'

'Complex? Oh, no, my dear Dr. Brooke, on the contrary, I feel within me the soul of La Brige.'

'Who is La Brige?'

'He is one of our national heroes.'

'A hero?'

'Yes, indeed! A hero of non-conformity, a humble and yet most respectable hero. I understand him now that I am in America.'

Dr. Brooke considered me with kindly concern. Then, suddenly seized anew by his American restlessness, he exclaimed: 'Since you are blue, we'll try to cheer you up. Monsieur Duhamel, get on your dinner-jacket. We must hurry now. You know that Americans never have any time to spare.'

'Unhappy Americans, how poor you are!'

Dr. Brooke's mouth opened: he seemed stupefied. 'Poor?' he said.

'Of course, my dear doctor. Time is the greatest wealth, and you never have any. You never have enough to spare any of it. You are dreadfully poor.'

The face of the doctor suddenly relaxed, and he laughed long and heartily: 'I understand your paradox,' said he.

'It is not a paradox, Dr. Brooke. It is the expression of the most heartfelt concern. It is time, it is high time, that America produced a few indolent persons — I mean dreamers who shall save it from itself.'

Dr. Brooke laughed heartily. 'That's good,' said he, 'that's very good. You say amusing things in such a serious way. But do hurry. Dinner is waiting for us at the club, and you know that they are to announce tonight the returns of the presidential election — a great occasion. Our club is a club of cultivated men — a picked crowd. We Americans who live in the large cities, men of good average position, are hardly able to entertain our friends at home, as the custom is in Europe. Our apartments are too small, and we have no servants. Remember that a maid-of-all-work, a Negro woman who works eight hours a day, gets high wages. You have to give her four dollars a day — say a hundred francs in your money — four dollars a day, her food, and her carfare. Oh, well! Our children are brought up in the open air in schools in the country. My wife, who is active in many ways, lives at her club, and I live at mine. When we want to take a meal at home, we go up to the restaurant on the eighteenth floor, where we are well looked after. What else can we do? A house — that is to say, a house as you understand the word on the other side of the ocean — is a most expensive luxury. Even to have children is rather ostentatious. You, too, begin to understand these things in Europe. So I have my club. There I entertain my friends, there I read the newspapers and the magazines, there I smoke and loaf. I have my special table, my own particular corner, the surroundings I am accustomed to — and, if you like, my home.'

'Yes, I understand. Driven by circumstances, you have put into practice a sort of bourgeois communism.'

Dr. Brooke threw an anxious glance round him. 'Communism,' he breathed. 'What do you mean by that? You do say such queer things.'

'I certainly said bourgeois communism. Though on a much more luxurious scale, of course, your clubs remind me of the houses for peasants, or indeed of the houses for writers, that you see in the big cities of the Soviets. The same suppression of the individual...'

'Frankly,' said Dr. Brooke with a sudden show of pride, 'we have solved the domestic problem in our own way, which seems to me reasonable, now that I've grown accustomed to it. We have almost got rid of household cares. We can busy ourselves with something else.'

'What else?'

'Why' — Dr. Brooke showed an astonished face — 'why, business, of course!' And he added with a vehement air of conviction, 'You are a man of liberal opinions; you cannot find fault with our doing away with the servant?'

'You haven't done away with him; you merely have him in common.'

'We demand less of him in this way.'

'Dr. Brooke, if it is a great disgrace to act as a servant, it's a greater disgrace to be served. I have been in the Southern States. They were finishing the cotton-picking. At that time, you know, the American women cannot keep a servant. The maids all leave, even the silliest Negro girls. They all go to look for good wages among the planters. They change masters. In the same way your former servants have merely changed masters. They are today the slaves of a different employer, a machine. They pass every hour of their lives in screwing down a bolt, turning a stopcock, or scraping the flank of a hog...'

Dr. Brooke was no longer listening; he was touching his hat right and left, for we had reached the club.

We took the inevitable elevator. Perhaps somewhere in the bulk of American buildings there are vestiges of stairs. It would take an expert searcher to find them. But you always find an elevator with its sickening leaps. You pass from one box into another box, from one cage into another cage.

Leaving the elevator we entered the cloakroom, as spacious as an Army Clothing Store; it is intimacy itself. During our brief stop in the resplendent wash-room, Dr. Brooke said, with an absent-minded air:

'You find fault with our system, but you'll surely be forced to come to it some day or other.'

'Eh? I know it. I feel it. And that is precisely what fills me with despair.'

On entering the dining-room of the club, the first thing I saw was an enormous silver-plated receptacle in which were plunged several long-handled ladles. Round it was a whole collection of glasses. Whenever the fancy took them, members of the company went to it and filled goblets with the pinkish liquor.

It was nine o'clock. A great restlessness reigned among the crowd of diners. Today a hundred million citizens were choosing their chief. The event was an excellent reason for generous libations of alcohol.

In a corner, at the table reserved by Dr. Brooke, his guests were awaiting us. After we had shaken hands, Dr. Brooke again dragged me off.

'The club,' said he, 'is private property. We can consequently drink whatever seems good to us. Come, let's have a taste of this potion.'

'Potion' was not so bad a name for it. The pink liquor that I took away in my glass was a synthetic alcohol, vaguely perfumed with some fruit essence. Such as it was, the fiery drink, distributed without limit and drunk without restraint, seemed already to have sensibly heated the company, accustomed though it was to mixtures less rich and less honest. I realized that my refusing to drink it put out and chagrined a little these attentive hosts, for whom the least drop of alcohol represented a sort of victory.

However, though disdained by me, the drink did not lack admirers. It was beginning to do its work. It reddened every face, inflamed every breath, and liberated every opinion. Every five minutes a volunteer in evening dress rose in the middle of the hall and announced the election returns. He shouted some confused figures that the crowd eagerly interpreted, for the men in dinner-jackets and the ladies with bare shoulders burst into cheers, but whether they expressed jubilation or anger there was no way to tell.

'We have,' said the doctor, 'the results in the East, which is a solar hour ahead of us in time. On the other hand, the results in the West, in California, for example, where it is hardly seven o'clock yet, will reach us late in the night. What can you do? The United States is big. The noise surprises you, perhaps.'

How could it have surprised me? Here it is at home. It is the king of the city, the real master of the country. Through the neighboring window I looked out at nocturnal Chicago, the thronging buildings that sprang up everywhere like so many geysers of fire. Ah, you poets of the Old World, you are able to imagine all things, the bottom of the sea, the desert, the moon; you cannot imagine Chicago, the ant-hill, the city that is not even ugly, but that is haggard and inhuman as a drunkard's nightmare.

I got a little respite through looking out the window, but not for long. The vociferations of the company would have awakened the dead.

The glasses of alcoholic drugs traveled from hand to hand. The colored waiters in turquoise-blue jackets raced round laden with things to eat. Every ten minutes the shouting gentleman leaped up like a jack-in-the-box, and told us how the people of New Jersey or of Connecticut had voted. The diners freed their jaws with a swallow and threw out a salvo of noise in honor of Smith or of Hoover. Then they called for music.

The music suddenly burst forth from a corner. It was the falsest, the shrillest, the most explosive of jazz — that breathless uproar which for many years now has staggered to the same syncopation, that shrieks through its nose, weeps, grinds its teeth, and caterwauls throughout the world. Jazz is a triumph of barbaric folly that has received praise, interpretation, and technical commentary from those educated musicians who, more than anything else, fear to be regarded as not in the last degree 'modern,' and thus to vex their clientèle, and who bow down to jazz as the painters of 1910 bowed down to cubism, for fear, as the phrase is, of missing the bus, and as the novelists of today bow down to the prevalent taste and introduce into all their stories a 'pair' of homosexuals and 'three-of-a-kind' of drug addicts.

Saxophone, drums, inebriated violin, cooing

piccolo — jazz had sounded its call, and, I beg you to believe, not in vain. There was commotion in the company. The old women rose first of all, with an ardor and an eagerness that you would not dare to expect from such venerable hips, such swollen ankles, and such sagging bosoms. O jazz, stimulant supreme! by what miracle have you driven back the hour of sunset, and raised all these ghosts?

These respectable ladies with their white hair — O moving moment! Do tell us all about it, Grandmamma! — began to stamp round in the open space among the tables. A long time afterwards the young women rose nonchalantly. They ventured to take a few disdainful steps in the crowd of dancers. A cry fused with the other cries. The proclamatory gentleman had climbed upon a chair. He announced that Maine and Virginia had declared their choice. All the dancers stopped for a moment to hail with generous clamor the name of Hoover or of Smith, and then again began their capering, while the jazz lost all decency and restraint and spat joyously in the face of music.

'They are having a good time,' said the benign Dr. Brooke, lifting his eyebrows. 'They are right to amuse themselves in the evening; they work so hard all day.'

'You're speaking of the men, my dear doctor, and I believe you. This afternoon I attended the symphony concert, and an excellent concert it was, too. There were more than a thousand women there, and I'm almost ashamed to say that there were only six men. I am positive, for I counted them.'

'Well, what can you expect, Monsieur Duhamel? Our men like to work.'

'That is what all these women say with a pretty, coaxing pout, just as they would say about their cat, "Poor little thing, she just loves mamma's milk." In short, we were only six men in the great concert hall. I was not too proud of myself: I looked like one of those effeminate æsthetes who take unmanly pleasures, while real men, seated in their offices, sell jars of preserves, as becomes the stronger sex.'

'Don't make fun of them! All these gentlemen whom you see enjoying themselves this evening have led all day a very hard and exacting life.'

'I can believe it. They even remind me of those men who would sell their souls in order to put a bigger mouthful of oleomargarine on their poppy-seed bun. Just now it is the hour of relaxation.'

'One has to laugh a little.'

'Ah, my dear doctor, you have made it clear

now. I did not know what was the matter with me. You have to laugh. And you should laugh! But just look at these people. They're *not* laughing. They shout, they dance, they eat, and they drink this poison, but they do not laugh. And I'm terribly afraid of a world in which men have forgotten how to laugh. You know as well as I do, they have founded in this country a "league to preserve the habit of laughter." What a revelation!'

'That's true,' said the doctor, thoughtfully nodding his head. 'Even if you have plenty of money, you can't be laughing every day. But you are eating scarcely anything. Yet it's all good here.'

'Excuse me, my dear Dr. Brooke. Everything is all right, except your guest. Who is the rather remarkable gentleman who is dancing with that young woman?'

'He's a business man here who has just married for the fifth time. That's not uncommon in the United States. When rightly understood, divorce is unquestionably a safeguard against adultery, which is not approved of in this country.'

'Really? And who is this astonishing lady?'

The doctor made a vague gesture. The woman whom I indicated with a slight nod wore on her fingers some of those diamonds which Americans call 'rocks' on account of their insolent size. And those prodigious jewels were bound to her wrist with solid, clinking gold chains. Her gown was gold and her slippers were gold. Of gold, too — red and green gold — was her old, a hundred times retinted hair. And behind all that jeweler's shop, I seemed to see a hundred thousand squealing pigs whose throats were being cut by a Negro all over blood.

It was not pigs that were screaming; it was the enthusiastic dancers. Once again they saluted with a long drink of alcohol the probable triumph of the champion of prohibition.

Should I let my glance follow the swaying dancers? Should I watch a while longer the behavior of that devastating brunette who is holding her partner's thumb in her firm clasp? No, I preferred rather to watch the crazy scene that was being played at the next table. A Jewess, still beautiful, though with a beauty that I can only describe as profaned, was trying to sell her daughter to a certain decrepit old man under the cold, gloomy, cruel eyes of two young men whose faces were full of hate. The 'transaction' seemed to need a good deal of hard work. The old robber, apparently, was deaf: he curved his hand round his hairy ear and had every word repeated to him. The procuress-mother put on her most captivating manners. The maiden — gown with panniers, shoulders slight but pure in line, delicate features, disdainful expression — conscientiously swallowed her disgust. The two *gigolos* — were they her brothers or her lovers? oh, how I wished I knew! — did not even make a pretense of eating; they had all they could do to swallow the bitter pill. Finally, the bargain seemed to be struck. The mother again looked at her daughter with half-shut eyes and offered her to the old man for that unexacting dance, the fox-trot. The pitiful puppet slowly set himself in motion. I was afraid that he would fall. A long shining thread of saliva hung from his lower lip down to his crumpled shirt-front. He talked, he promised, he made offers. With a movement of her eyelids the young girl said yes — a smiling, disdainful, indifferent yes, full of rancor. The old man panted and grew purple as if he were going to die. And two hundred thousand hogs, sacrificed behind the scenes, celebrated the agreement with a deafening clamor.

The jazz went roaring on. The rose-tinted alcohol poured down the throats. The Negro waiters in their dark blue jackets slipped among the dancers with strained faces, staring eyes, and drops of sweat on their nostrils. Gusts of noisy clamor announced from time to time that the champion of total abstinence was gaining ground. At other times, intoxicated with the swooning saxophone, a part of the company shrieked 'The Sidewalks of New York,' lugubrious twaddle that is reputed to be the favorite tune of Mr. Smith.

The doctor whispered amiably in my ear, 'Don't you find this great fun?'

I felt not the least inclination to reply. My head was cool, my eye was clear, and I was quite unaffected by any drug unworthy of a drinker of true and noble wine. I gazed through the window at the nocturnal city, unbridled and shaken with all the furies and with all the lusts that seemed to me to be seeking everywhere, even in the rain-sodden clouds, the phantom of joy, pure human joy forever driven from the world.

X

FIREWORKS

OR

THE EXTRAVAGANCES OF ADVERTISING

In the daytime the sun makes them powerless, but the night is their own. They have divided among themselves the Kingdom of Darkness. Now here, now there, they begin to awake with the twilight. With the serene persistence of machines, they resume their work of propaganda, of intimidation, in a *charivari* of light, a riot, a battle, a triumph of disharmony and disorder. Discipline does not rise above the ground; it does not rise above the crawling multitude. In the Kingdom of Darkness, there is no law but that of the strongest. It is the jungle, with all its savagery.

Here are the elephants and the hippopotami, the great unrivaled pachyderms of publicity who dominate everything by mere sheer bulk. Here are the powerful brutes: the lions and tigers. Here are the lean and shifty foxes of the stories. Here, finally, are the apes, who know not what fresh acrobatics to invent to catch the bewildered gaze of the passer-by.

Some, like a card-sharper, spread out their whole pack, card by card, and then shuffle it with a single turn of the wrist. Some juggle with words, tossing them up and catching them again without ever missing — an inhumanly monotonous performance. Others, every two or three minutes, give the latest political news, the racing results, the time, or some other piece of information for which no one has asked them. Others seek to seduce us, to challenge us, to wear us down, to irritate us, to take us unaware, to conquer us, and to convince us they do not care how. They leap, fall back, are born, die, turn, wriggle, bound, straighten themselves, fall to pieces, burst, bud, decompose, recompose, change color, rhythm, gait or speed, wink, flap their wings, stamp their foot, or shake their belly, draw in their breath, sing, cry, eructate — all with grimaces, nervous jerks, contractions, spasms, designed by the epileptic and the hysteric, the drunkard and the madman.

'Dr. Brooke,' I said, 'to me the moment seems to have arrived for founding, first of all in the United States, and later in the whole world, a league to protest against impertinent advertising. Yes, I am quite sane, and you have heard what I said. Shall the great law of reaction that applies to phenomena of every kind keep silence about this tremendous business of coercion and brutalization? Let us lay the foundations of our league, my dear doctor, while I am still treading the free soil of America. Let us make a supreme effort, I beg you, to defend these holy things now ruined, or in decay — the horizon, quiet, reverie, courtesy, elegance, smiles, free will, the virgin wall, and white paper. Devil take it, the domain of advertising merely begins where my patience, my enjoyment, and my good will end. We ought not to put up with these encroachments.

'You, who with your motley hoardings conceal the landscape from me, shall not have my custom. You, who foul the silence, as if no one had a right to it, shall be quarantined, as you should be. You, who abuse my confidence by urging me to read twenty lines that end in a trap, indemnify me at once, make me laugh, or fear my anger! You, who dirty the very windows of the bus, you need not hope to escape on easy terms! You are down on my list; I denounce you both for your impudence and for your clumsiness.

'I am not ill-natured, but I am obstinate, and I insist on doing what I want to do, what I will to do, and to do only what I will to do. A comrade, a neighbor at a hotel table, a chance companion who, showing off, reveals a little fatuity, or presumption, or craft — ah, how quick we are to

enough to prevent any one from hearing anything. You Americans cannot easily imagine that festival, for it so happens that you often carry on your financial operations in a room of no more than two hundred square feet, smoking your cigar before the board on which the quotations are listed. Understand clearly; at the Paris Bourse every one uses his voice simply to make a noise. And so true is that remark, that all that remains to the habitués of the place is to express their meaning with gestures. The clamor of the Bourse, its shameful hullabaloo, is wasted breath, energy misused with no benefit to any one. Very well — oh, I'm not wandering from my subject! — the greatest part of publicity as it is practiced today is energy misused without benefit to the common run of men — energy, however, that we must all pay for in some degree.

'At the beginning, doubtless, those who first employed the tricks of publicity won an advantage over their rivals. But today, when all the world pays tribute to the new religion, the effect of publicity grows less, and becomes neutralized. Like every habitual stimulant, it is bound at last to lose its power to excite. Hence come these extravagant exaggerations. And in the end we all pay for this new human folly. We pay for these hateful noises, these insolent lights, these shameless proposals, these cynical injunctions, this lack of consideration, these intrusions, these obsessions, these lapses from delicacy, these importunities, and these insults.

'Dr. Brooke, I repeat the word insult. No other word fits the case. That modern commercial methods strive to harness and prostitute reputation, assuredly is pitiable. It is pitiable, too, that in the last count they force me to bear the expense of their extravagance. I am vexed, but I am resigned. And how can I help being resigned? The point from which I feel that I will not permit myself to budge is this: modern publicity shows an insulting contempt for the public. It treats man as if he were the most stupid of the inferior animals. What! I have acute senses, educated and made subtle by the practice of the noblest arts. I am one of those who can divine, translate, recognize relations, analyze, follow a trail, detect a symptom, and catch an allusion. In a word, I am a man, and, as Unamuno said, "nothing less than a man and a whole man." Is it for me, this publicity of flashes, repetitions, and explosions, that seem conceived to excite the reflexes of a sedentary mollusk? Are these titillations, this tickling, this burlesque — a kind of masturbation of the eye — for me? Let me laugh! Let me laugh!

'Dr. Brooke, your compatriots have given the most luxurious development to those big amusement parks where, in exchange for their dollars, citizens go to be driven round, shaken, pulverized, and pounded — in short, to be brutalized. I cannot think of those practices without humiliation. Are such tossing and jolting needed to distract a man and to stir him? Do we consecrate our senses to such usage? Have you ever seen the most miserable of curs sniff round a post? What delicacy, what infinite care! He chooses, he does not take it all, but just a sniff of air, the merest whiff of the odor. The dog does not use his senses coarsely, I assure you. But we men? We want to be shaken to pieces, stood on our heads, whirled, to be spun like a top, to be dazzled and blinded. It takes nothing less than that to stir us. Pah!

'My dear Dr. Brooke, modern publicity reminds me of all the Luna Parks, all the Magic Cities, of Europe, and especially all those of America. It gives too gross, too despicable an idea of man. I emphatically decline to bear such a stigma, and propose to you that we form a league. Shame on those shopkeepers who think to wheedle and win us by regarding us as idiots.

'My dear doctor, I foresee that you are going to tell me that I shall be the only member of my league. Alas, that is quite possible. Let us leave this avenue, I beg. Let us escape this obscene press-gang of lights. Let us slip into this cross-street that publicity neglects, and that from that very circumstance looks like a thieves' kitchen. At least we'll be at our ease, at least I shall be able to read to you, under the simple light of a lamp-post, some lines from a philosopher who is a compatriot of yours, Thomas S. Baker. For, you know, the misfortunes of America never cease tormenting some true Americans. "The methods of the manufacturer," says this worthy man, "are carried into the domain of letters and journalism, and, thanks to the prodigious art of American advertising and to the efforts of high-pressure salesmen, persons of no importance are exploited by men whom you might call literary merchants as skillfully and sometimes as profitably as patent medicines."

'Dr. Brooke, you think that our American has not discovered America. He points out a peril to which the whole world is accustomed; that is, resigned. If publicity gets its grip on the things of the mind, the reason is that the things of the mind are weakly defended. If they are badly defended, the reason is that they are hardly things of the "mind."

'That, my dear doctor, is a subject on which it

is my privilege to have a firm, lively, and sharp-edged opinion. I have seen the American method disembark, if I may use the term, in Western Europe. Be sure that I am not going either to complain or to scold. I am neither Cassandra nor Jeremiah. But I shall laugh, and heartily, if the mood takes me. I have seen the book merchants behave like merchants: that is, strive by every method to sell their books. You know the result; certain men of letters, losing all decency and even honor, have permitted the fruit of their agony to be offered to the public like a mere piece of goods, vaunted by mouths that are mercenary, and injudicious, and anonymous to boot. In the rage for increased profit artists who are not lacking in talent and in intelligence have rivaled the manufacturers of chocolates and *apéritifs*. To abuse the public confidence has suddenly seemed to them quite natural, even praiseworthy. I merely make an effort to grasp and understand the phenomenon.

'Faithful from the beginning to the principles of that famous league of which I am the only member, I resist in my own way. I refuse to read books, even though they come from a skillful or a famous pen, that seem to me presented to the public in an unbecoming manner. Like every one else, I think that the author is perhaps grasping, avaricious, and weak in the face of his own appetite. I think, moreover, that he is not curious; he is not curious to know what is the value of his naked soul.

'The life of a writer, an artist, is a long experiment, a fascinating game that is played between a mind and the world. Well! I wish my experiment to remain pure. That is my principal interest. I refuse to introduce into my equation those indeterminate factors which would falsify all my calculations. I do not speak in a desert; a multitude is listening to me. Very well, then! That multitude and I are at close grips with each other. Leave us in peace to play our game out honestly. Let no one mark the cards. Let no one seek by trickery to give me more than I am worth, more than I deserve. I wish to deceive no one, least of all myself. Let me alone, then, to come to an understanding with those who like me and do me the honor to read me. Above all, do not tell them that my latest book "is perhaps the most astonishing book that has been published in the whole world since the twelfth century." There is only one thing that matters to me — to refuse to pass for something that I am not. As a wise man whom I know said, in effect, "If by surprise, by a trick, we force ten thousand persons to read a work for which they have neither need nor liking, we make ten thousand persons dissatisfied, we gain ten thousand enemies."

'That, my dear Dr. Brooke, is one of those illusory calculations, the privilege of which I leave to those impenitent dreamers whom we call business men.'

XI

THE SEGREGATION OF RACES

HERE was the Head Mistress.

She was an old lady, still very active, even graceful. She wore a long gown of reddish-brown watered silk. Like a pure-bred Cévinole — like my wife's mother — she had beautiful light blue eyes, and smooth bands of white hair. Her hands were slender and delicate, the nails touched with mauve. She was fairer than a woman of Provence. If she had been standing in the Paris 'Métro,' the surliest lout would have given her his seat. Obviously she had authority. I was to learn that she had education, and I could see at once that she had breeding.

Breeding? Where had she got it? She was a Negress, nothing more — a white Negress. In her nostrils and her lower lip there was almost nothing to suggest Negro blood; almost nothing, but much more than enough. In all New Orleans there was not a single person in good society to shake hands in public with this respectable old lady.

Meanwhile, the old lady was showing us her school. It was a fine school, well built, and well managed, staffed with good teachers, all of whom, of course, were more or less colored. Not a single pure-blooded white had been misguided enough to enter that shameful world. In a well-modulated and dignified voice the old lady told us the daily problems of her school — the excess of pupils, and all the other difficulties of the present and of the future.

'Will you do us the honor, gentlemen,' she said by way of concluding our visit, 'to try the cooking of our older pupils, and take your luncheon here?'

Mr. Lionel and I accepted the courteous invitation. We were led into a hall where two covers were laid. And as we stood there, the old lady brought forward two chairs. There followed a long moment of embarrassment.

'Madam,' I said at last, 'have you already had your luncheon?'

The old lady's face slightly paled. Her lower lip — the traitorous lip — slightly quivered. With an almost imperceptible shake of her head, she indicated that she had not yet eaten.

'Madam,' said I again, 'won't you do us the honor of sharing with us the luncheon that you have offered us?'

Our hostess, visibly embarrassed, stammered some words in English. Finally, her face recovered composure. She smiled a child's smile, in which there appeared now humility, now confusion, now gratitude. She accepted a chair.

'I should never have dared,' she murmured. 'I should never have hoped...'

Since I was not accustomed to such scenes, I felt myself blushing.

Mr. Richard C. Lionel is what they call in this country a creole; that is, he is descended from French colonists, and has not the slightest trace of black blood. He belongs to that ancient Louisiana society which still speaks of city 'blocks' as 'islets,' and which at home speaks the French of the eighteenth century, a French soon to be swamped under the ponderous Anglo-Saxon wave.

'Don't get into that street car,' he said to me.

'Why?'

'It's a "Jim Crow" car; one, that is, especially for Negroes. Look at this shop.'

'What's unusual about it?'

'Nothing, except that it's a shop for Negroes. And the movie theater you see yonder is a theater exclusively for the colored people.'

'Why "exclusively"? Let's go in.'

'Don't do that. Even the Negroes themselves would not think it fitting. You would have the air either of a ridiculous demagogue, or else of going to look at these people as you might go to look at some curious animals. Tomorrow, you're taking the train for Texas. You will see that even in the small stations there is a special waiting-room for "colored people." Only here in the South can you understand the Negro problem, and estimate its seriousness. In my family, we have always treated the colored people with kindness and pity, like domestic animals. I am pretty independent, myself. You noticed that I shook hands with the head mistress of the school.'

'She is hardly a Negress. She's like the sweetest old ladies at home.'

'All the same, she's a colored woman! You see, that unexpectedly reappears many generations later, no one knows why. It's like a curse. I have friends in Wisconsin, one of the Northern States, however, where things are quite different. These were friends of mine, I tell you. They had no children. So they adopted a little girl, a beautiful little girl, and white, of course. Time passed and the little girl attained her eighteenth year. That is the age when the least trace of Negro blood shows itself. The little white girl suddenly proved to be "colored." The signs of race appear, you see, with sexual maturity. There was nothing, or almost nothing, to show her race;

about her nose, mouth, and fingers, a mere shadow, an evil memory. Poor child! She didn't know herself what was the matter. She had been brought up as a young lady. Between one day and the next disaster had stricken her: society was closed against her. And the foster-parents, although distressed, made their arrangements, and they, too, withdrew from her. Every hope of marriage, except with one of her black brothers, was gone. Can you imagine a misfortune like that? The girl did everything she could to kill herself — almost the only solution. You understand; it's the terrible segregation of the races, but necessary, I assure you, absolutely necessary.'

'I do not deny it. But it should have been done at the start; that is, two or three centuries ago.'

'Come and see the old cemeteries of New Orleans.'

It was a graveyard of French memories. It was a Catholic cemetery. All Saints' Day had come once again to decorate it. The flowers were dying in the humid heat. As the marshy soil is unfit for the purpose of burial, the bodies have to waste away in tiers of boxes built above the ground. A poignant melancholy exhaled from this retreat, which the noise and bustle of the great modern city did not reach.

It is the burial-place of a race and of a civilization. The epitaphs tell in laconic French all sorts of mishaps, trials, epidemics, all sorts of sufferings endured for the conquest of this bitter land. Under one and the same date you read: 'Paul, Lucie, Joseph: Three Angels. And their Mother.' There is no commentary, or even a family name. A fine moss of a brilliant green covered the neighboring stones.

Well, even in death, the races must be separated. At home, the different religions divide the soil within a common enclosure; it is their last effort, the last outburst of aversion. Here, the horror strikes deeper. The Negroes have their own graveyard apart, with its walls, its gate, its part of the swamp, and its solitude. There is nothing in common among the races, even in dissolution — nothing, that is, unless it be that sorrowful, impotent cross which, in spite of walls, presents on either side of the street an identical sign of impossible union.

At Tuskegee in Alabama I measured the whole extent of the tragedy. A two hours' carriage-drive from Montgomery is necessary to reach this citadel of Negro thought. It is not Jerusalem, or Mecca, or Rome; it is a modest little town, or not so much as that — a big village. It is even less and much more: a college. I do not say 'university.' It is a simple secondary and occupational school, at which fifteen hundred black students are lodged, taught, and provided with a little of that knowledge which makes masters.

I saw them all gathered in the refectory, spacious as the nave of a cathedral. They were all standing before their plates where smoked sweet potatoes and tomato sauce. They sang for me under the direction of a gray-haired master: they sang their 'spirituals,' the Christian hymns of the days of slavery. They are sad hymns which are often beautiful, and in which, in spite of the words, the harsh, barbarous, and mysterious voice of Africa often wails.

What diversity there is in this black race! All the tribes that were formally raided by the slave-traders had some representative in that strange assembly. Many centuries of intermarriage have engendered disorder and even incoherence, but yet have not lessened the vigor of certain types. You see strange silhouettes — from the anthropoid, all neck and jaws, to the fine aquiline face, pure, open, and tortured by the problems of the mind. All were assembled there, ever marked with the brand of slavery, and all prisoners of their skin. All were there from the female idol of ebony, fine and beautiful as an Egyptian queen, down to the female servant sculptured in coal — fat-cheeked, broad-hipped, full-breasted and monumental — who wore her hair completely stiff and straight because she and her kind take out the kink with drugs from New York, in order to have a fashionable appearance.

More plentiful than the pure-blooded Negroes are those of mixed race, innumerable witnesses to the sin of Americans. There is a swarm of half and quarter breeds, a living remorse, a living reproach to this people that, for well-founded reasons, repudiates mixed marriages. There are all the shades, all the mixtures — the drop of milk in the ink-well, the drop of ink in the milk-jug.

Those whom you cannot regard without discomfort and without shame are the ones who have reached the doorsill of the white paradise, but who, in spite of so many efforts and some favorable chances, have been unable to cross it and to become fused with the dominant race. They are there in the classes and in the offices at Tuskegee, the white Negroes, who in France would be taken for Levantines or Semites, but whom America has detected and sent back to the kennel. They are there also, the blonde Negresses with their tow heads, their pallid complexions, their sometimes too black eyes, and their too long and too stiff fingers so curiously turned up at the ends.

Why do all these disinherited creatures hesitate to scatter through the world and seek a true fatherland, one that will not curse them? That is the question that I pondered as I left, while from all the walls there gazed down upon me the elder Dumas, that honorable writer in whose veins flowed Negro blood, and President Roosevelt, who did an heroic act in shaking the hand of Booker T. Washington, founder of Tuskegee and prophet of the black race.

Who can leave Tuskegee without curiosity, without anxiety? I was surprised to find myself, with sharpened eyes, analyzing, feature by feature, every one whom I met. Has that proud lady who is so vain of her dollars a nose somewhat too short? Is not that gentleman's hair much too curly? And was it only the sun of Montgomery that gave its golden tint to the skin of this pompous parson?

In my hotel bedroom that night I lit all the lamps, I thought out various arrangements of mirrors, and in each in turn I examined myself, full face, profile, back, and three quarters. I examined my hands and my finger-nails. I contemplated every part of my person with the utmost care. Confound it, you never could tell...

Well, no! There was nothing that showed. My ancestors were surely peasants of Île-de-France. During several centuries, perhaps, they saw no other Negroes than those in the almanacs. But how was I to avoid doubting everything and every one, even myself, in this big, mixed America where the races, brought face to face, have not sought to understand one another, and have not succeeded in loving one another?

The North is more tolerant of Negroes than the South, and, moreover, less overrun with them. In a college in Connecticut I noticed a pretty little Negress among the graceful, doll-like whites.

After tea had been served, according to the custom of the place, the students put to me many questions that I answered as best I could. The little Negress questioned me in her turn. She was charming and well-dressed. In spite of her stigmata she had the self-assurance of the children of the rich. She looked at me proudly.

'Why is it that you, Monsieur,' she said in excellent French, 'who they say have such liberal ideas, spoke in your "Civilization" of your colored stretcher-bearers, as "savages"?'

There was a silence. All the young ladies whose faces were white showed by their discreet smiles their delight in the indiscreet question.

'Well,' I said, 'you see, Mademoiselle, they were Malagasies, if I remember right. And I described them as savages, because that is precisely what at least my stretcher-bearers were.'

A new silence. She of the black eyes threw me a glance of warm reproach; her full lips contracted.

'Oh,' said I, by way of consolation, 'if it is the word that troubles you, we have savages also among people of our own color.'

That drop of balm was not enough. The young girl went away, shaking her curly head, too full of her just grievance to be reasonable.

Mr. Oliver Knickerbocker is one of those men whom the Negro question keeps awake at night. He is a big, cold, forbidding man. He suffers from a repressed anger that makes him hot about the ears.

'No true American,' he said, 'will in any circumstances admit the idea of miscegenation. We are going to create the civilization of the future. We shall accomplish that great work with white blood. Every people that accepted cross-breeding has fallen into decay. Our safety resides in an unrelenting divorce of the races.'

'Well,' said I, 'you are quite right, but your six million Negroes are highly prolific. At no very distant day they will number twenty millions. What will you do with a burden like that huge herd?'

Mr. Oliver Knickerbocker shrugged his shoulders. 'We have,' he said, 'faced every possible solution. We have discussed buying an island somewhere to which to deport — or, let us say, in which to install — the whole race.'

'That's the solution of an impractical idealist.'

'Obviously. We have discussed surgical sterilization of the males.'

'That's a farcical solution. And the non-males, if I may use the expression?'

'There are even persons who propose more radical measures still.'

'I get your meaning. They are crazy.'

'Crazy, if you like.'

'Consequently, the problem...'

'Can't be solved.'

'It seems to me that for a true civilization the solution of such a problem as this would be a more important victory than cutting a canal through the Isthmus of Panama, or building a city, or inventing a new flying-machine.'

My companion stiffly shook his head. 'The problem,' he said, 'is insoluble — in — sol — u — ble!'

There was a long silence, during which Mr. Knickerbocker chewed his cigar.

'Mr. Knickerbocker,' I said in a low tone.

'Monsieur Duhamel.'

'The idea that the problem is insoluble need not perhaps wholly discourage us.'

'Be so kind as to explain...'

'Until this moment I have never had any assured belief in immanent justice. Until now I did not believe that every fault is punished in the end. I even saw in that belief an element of pessimism. All that you have been telling me creates a sort of hope. The idea that the unnumbered crimes of the slave-trade and of slavery that were the foundation of American prosperity cannot be expiated, and that those crimes have pierced the side of American happiness with an incurable wound — do you not find that, from the moral point of view, the idea is consolatory, and, all things considered, beautiful?'

Mr. Knickerbocker's ears turned red and then white. He looked at me a moment, opened a mouth full of gold, and sank into thought.

XII

THE MODERN TEMPLE

FROM far, far away, through the trumpeting of the autumn wind, through the raucous outcry and wrathful expostulations of ten thousand automobiles quarreling for precedence, you could distinguish the murmur of the stadium, its clamors and its storms.

It was a dirty, cluttered, disorderly sort of place, on the edge of the town. There in a great shapeless patch of ground was the stadium that the crowd held like a captured fortress. It was not the Coliseum, or the proud amphitheater of El Djem in its thirsty plain. It belonged to that sort of architecture which is cynically frank about its utilitarian purpose; an enormous, and, you would say, a fragile shell of concrete, open to the sky, and hidden under a thick, swarming layer of human flesh.

We had passed through the turnstile, for the god of the place exacts a pretty heavy obolus. We had made our way along corridors and up stairways, and had finally come into the open air.

The greatest multitude that I have ever seen was assembled there, ranked and disciplined by a ritual that was almost religious. In comparison with it, what are the crowds of the theater or of the concert, of the political rally, or even of the church — or, better still, even of the cinema? Indeed, I had found one of the temples of modern America.

What high, ennobling thought had gathered there so huge an assemblage? What passions had distorted all those faces, and strained all those throats with cheering; what hopes, what hatreds? For a moment I closed my eyes that I might feel, as if deep within me, that mighty crowd, that I might better perceive its sighs, its bursts of joy or rage; not that I might let myself be intoxicated, but rather that I might be carried away, swept off my feet, perhaps rocked by this wave of humanity. Then I emerged from it.

Scattered over a grassy field checkered with white lines, twenty-two men were playing football. As well as I could judge from where I was, they were young men. Their heads were protected with padded helmets and their shins with something like the Roman greave. On their jerseys were large labels, each bearing a number.

The game was not radiant, gay, airy; rather it was grim, savage, and self-contained. Twenty-two men were on the field, in two opposing rows. For an appreciable time they remained motionless in strange postures. They seemed to watch one another like dogs pointing. Then the ball was thrown. There followed a struggle — very short, very confused, and indescribably brutal. There was nothing in it to suggest the grace of a dance, or of a Greek statue. It had no elegance, no imagination, above all, no beauty, unless it were that repellent beauty you may find at times in a display of savagery. And suddenly a whistle blew, the pack was immobile, tense, and watching its prey again before another tussle.

That is what you see in the field. But for me, the impenitent outsider, the show was not what was happening in the field. It was on the stands with the crowd. How many of them were there? Forty, fifty thousand persons, or perhaps more; I cannot say. The university of the city had challenged the university of a neighboring State. Each of the two tribes, brought face to face, had hoisted its oriflamme. The girl students were on the left, the boys were on the right. The common herd filled the gigantic shell. The plebeian crowd, without distinction and without authority, was there, and knew that it was there, only as ballast, as padding, as the odd change that made up the bill. In it you could recognize and count five hundred times the same masculine hat — gray with a black ribbon — and a thousand times the same feminine hat — the same blue, the same shape, the same trimming — and in fact all the stock articles forced on them by the local shopkeepers. In short, here was the mob in all its colorless horror.

The aristocratic element in such an assembly is, today, the students, with their colors, their glee clubs, their bands with grotesque instruments, their songs, and the organized cheering that the two tribes use to incite the men on the field. Each group has its captain, its cheerleader. That is an enviable distinction. The happy incumbent is provided with a megaphone, like a ballyhoo-man at a fair. For the benefit of the crowd, he comments on all the phases of the match, announces the scores, or the penalties, lets loose, or moderates, the enthusiasm, and by his witticisms and his gestures stimulates the reflexes of the public.

At the game I attended, the powdered and rouged girl students sat in line on the cement steps of the Stadium, like parrakeets on a perch. From their bosoms, still as immature as apples in July, they sent forth shrill penetrating cries that seemed to have a tonic influence on the nerves of the competitors. The leader of these young girls was decidedly pretty. She bore, they told me, one of the most honorable names in the country.

With a megaphone in her hand, and with her skirts flying in the wind, she screamed, flounced about, gave play to leg and haunch, and performed a suggestive and furious *dance du ventre*, like the dances of the prostitutes in the Mediterranean ports. From time to time she reassembled her aviary, and encouraged it to a fresh outburst of shrill screaming.

I do not know this game of football, famous though it is throughout the world. What those madmen were doing down there in the field seemed to me not in the least to warrant all that indecent vociferation. The greater part of the public knew scarcely more than I of what was going on, did not see clearly, and did not understand. Sometimes, the birds took flight at the wrong moment and made mistakes, hooted when they should have applauded, approved when they should have protested. Many chattered; others yawned. Then the glee clubs let themselves go, and with their shrill piping covered the noisy chatter of the spectators. Next, the young men, stressing each syllable, shouted in unison the distinctive cheer, the 'slogan' of the tribe. And meanwhile the sturdy fellows on the gridiron continued like furious ants hotly to dispute the big leathern egg.

What did they all want? What did those thousands of men and women come for? Was it really to watch the dangerous struggle between two clans of students that all that crowd rushed there, paid money, sat patiently, and stamped its feet on the cement in the chill of the late afternoon?

Did you not come, O crowd, rather to get drunk on yourselves, on your own voice, on your own noise; to feel yourselves numerous and full of strength, to be charged with one another's emanations, and to taste the mysterious pleasures of the herd, the hive, and the ant-hill?

And, after all, what did that sport amount to in which twenty-two stout fellows struggled breathlessly, while forty thousand persons sat immobile, caught cold, smoked cigarettes, and exercised nothing except their vocal cords? To be sure, they reminded me of the men who are referred to in France as enthusiastic, or distinguished, sportsmen because twice a week they go to see horses gallop, and thereby lose some hundreds of francs, with the complicity of the public authorities. I am not one of those crotchety scholars who never use their muscles, who are either lazy or timid, and whom all physical effort bores and depresses. I have traveled over most of Europe with a knapsack on my back. Like every sensible man, I can swim, ride a bicycle, drive a car, use a racket, and even an oar. For years I have made the floor of a *salle d'armes* echo with my endeavors to give a city man's body some honest fatigue. I fully intend that if circumstances permit, my three sons shall be quick, supple, and robust. No, I do not despise physical exercise; I love it, I recommend it, and I often yearn for it from the depth of a too studious retirement. But I admit that this comedy of sport with which the youth of the world is befooled and fascinated seems to me more than a little idiotic.

In proportion as sport goes hand-in-hand with hygiene and morals, it becomes a personal, modest affair, or even a game of easy-going companions, an occasion of friendly rivalry, and especially a pleasure — in the sense that the word bore before it took on its modern meaning — and an amusement, a matter of gayety and recreation. At the hands of ingenious exploiters, sport has become the most profitable of spectacles. And as a necessary corollary, it has become the most astonishing school of vanity. The joyously acquired habit of performing the least important acts of a game before a crowd of onlookers has bred in a youth poorly protected against wild extravagances, all the faults that only yesterday were attributed to the most conceited of second-rate actors. A very odd shift has occurred in popular interest. What light opera tenor, what fashionable or notorious novelist, what master of political oratory, can boast today of being so famous, so flattered, and so caricatured as the gentlemen of the ring, of the stadium, and of the track. I am not speaking of the great athletes, those who do some particular feat exceptionally well, those who invent something new, those who have elements of inspiration, who create a new manner or leave a tradition, and those who show themselves great by patience, by courage, by grace, or by imagination. No, I am speaking of those worthy lads who keep goal decently, who can run a hundred yards well enough, or who can pedal a bicycle for a long time — and who can no longer open a newspaper without hunting for their picture, and the account of their Sunday exploits. I speak of those fine fellows who from babyhood have been in love with strength, suppleness, skillful play, the graceful and difficult feat, and who little by little have been spoiled by pride, led to engage in absurd competitions, delivered over to the worst of publics, that of the circus, made drunken with a crude and treacherous glory that soon becomes more tyrannical than alcohol. I speak of

obliged to choose between an obscure employment in some trade, and the hope of some day becoming a football captain, would keep his serenity? Who would not drop the unattractive substance for the delightful shadow?

To encourage our French youth to adopt the cult of sport, we have put into play all the well-worn tricks. We have declared that our impoverished and threatened country may some time need a hardy youth, tempered by the sports that require strength and address — but, if we apply to the argument the test of history, we find that it is valueless. For France, at least, the World War was fought by peasants, clerks, workingmen, middle-class people, and intellectuals, most of whom had no training in sports, and who for almost five years displayed physical and moral qualities worthy of respect. On the other hand, certain of the kings of sport did not so much as risk their greatness by sharing the sufferings of the common people.

Among all the grievances that this curious discussion brings to notice we cannot pass over in silence the eternal question of language. Those who make a profession of sport have acclimatized in France an astounding jargon that is almost untranslatable, that is larded with foreign words used inappropriately and ridiculously pronounced, and that is a tangle of metaphors that good sense — I say nothing of good taste — disavows.

Immediately after the war a group of writers made a gallant attempt to provide sport with a readable literature. It was a great plan, but it was quickly abandoned. The cultivated public did not encourage their Olympic effusions, and the public of the grand-stands cares nothing whatever for *belles-lettres*. As for the actors in these muscular orgies, what has gone to their heads is an incense very different from that offered by young novelists; they did not so much as open the books that celebrated only the thing itself, and that did not always mention names. As, after all, authors write in the hope of being read, the disappointed novelists abandoned the field to the sports reporters.

Alas, alas! young men of France, have I not been in America? A little while ago was I not still in the big concrete crater that they call a stadium, surrounded with screaming girls and student choruses, and the unbridled crowd? Am I much to be blamed if tonight my remonstrances speed across the sea?

XIII

INSURANCE

OR

THE LAW OF COMPENSATION

'My dear man, do you mean to tell me that our great express train rolls along the boulevard itself, crosses the streets, and marches through the middle of the city, as if it owned it?'

'Yes, as if it owned it. That's quite simple, isn't it? In America everything is so simple.'

'And there are never any accidents?'

'Oh, yes, there are plenty.'

I sank back in my seat in the Pullman, temporarily routed. The Pullman is a car intended for long journeys, a drawing-room on wheels, in which the traveler remains all day. At night, the beds are made up. It is a sort of communism of the rich. The wash-room of the men provides for five persons at a time, like the common wash-room of the House of Scholars at Moscow. The Americans have not yet learned that the supreme luxury is privacy.

The train was now running through the country, and my astonishment was again aroused.

'What, my dear Mr. Stone, the railway crosses

other railways on their own level, and even at right angles?'

'You object to right angles?'

'And the roads, too?'

'Of course.'

'And that really does cause a lot of accidents?'

'A great many.'

'Oh, and the railway companies...?'

Most of the Americans whom I had met up to that time were, as a rule, of the kind that is described as 'intellectuals.' Mr. Stone, my polite and friendly companion, was exclusively a man of business; and did not wish to be taken for anything else. His person, his clothes, his baggage, his gestures, and his talk — everything about him in fact — tended to give you the impression of hard and concentrated, yet untroubled, thought — thought that, indeed, was little less than sublime. It was exclusively devoted to the manufacture and sale of wire spring mattresses. Mr. Stone was assured of a name in the history of spring mattresses. He was one of the men who through judicious calculation and vigorous action had reduced the kinds of spring mattresses adopted throughout the Union from seventy-eight to four. Moreover, Mr. Stone had so acute a genius in the field of trade and publicity that he could sell a spring mattress to any one he met. Whenever Mr. Stone looked at me somewhat fixedly, I felt troubled to the very depths of my soul; I had a dim feeling that something was lacking to my happiness; for example, a hundred spring mattresses. I had to make a considerable effort not to yield to the luxury of ordering some.

Oddly enough, Mr. Stone's thought seemed to stray from the spring mattresses. He opened his mouth, and, as he was an orderly man, he completed the phrase I had left unfinished.

'The railways have figured it all out. As to the accidents that result from this arrangement — grade crossings — it costs the companies less to pay insurance than to do the work that changing the roads would require. You see; that settled it.'

'Figures,' said I, 'of course are decisive. Yet it seems to me that figures do not cover every aspect of the question.'

Mr. Stone's voice took on its most serious tone. 'Why,' he asked, 'do you want to introduce into your calculations sentimental considerations that can't properly be reduced to figures, and that threaten to falsify your arithmetic without helping any one?'

Mr. Stone regarded me with an inquisitional eye. Should I have to buy half a dozen spring mattresses to appease him? My conscience was uneasy. However, I renewed my attack, though I shifted it to his flank.

'Do you not think,' said I, 'that the system of insurance helps more than a little to lower the standard of public morals?'

'I can't see,' he exclaimed, 'how public morality is offended when insurance settles a loss that otherwise might have no chance of fair compensation. You say insurance weakens morality; I think it works for justice. I am a convinced advocate of insurance. I have, of course, taken out all the insurance that the law requires, and also all that good sense recommends. I carry a heavy insurance against the loss of my physical or mental health. I have insured the members of my family, my domestic animals, and every object to which I feel attached; I am insured against every eventuality and phenomenon capable of exercising any considerable influence on my life. I insist that the people round me take precautions that I regard as elementary. For example, I do not spy on my employees to find out whether they are honest. Am I to trust to their conception of good and evil, to the scruples of their conscience? No. I require that each one of them be insured for a sum corresponding to the harm he can do me.'

'Mr. Stone, allow me to point out that, in your turn, and in spite of your finding the words irritating, you have introduced "good" and "evil" into your mathematical combinations; that is, elements that you rightly designate as imponderable. A French philosopher, Henri Bergson, at the beginning of one of his most famous books, asks in what respect, and for what reason, intensity is comparable to quantity. Listen carefully, Mr. Stone; Bergson is seeking what there can be in common between the extensive, which by definition is something that has extent, and which, consequently, can be measured, and the intensive, which is without extent, and which, consequently, is subject to no measure. Well, Mr. Stone, to that question insurance makes an answer that I find disquieting, but that all the rest of the world is beginning to approve: according to the insurance people, the common measure between the extensive and the intensive is money. Do you want an example? Your car knocks down a garden gate. That has extent; it is so many feet at so many dollars a foot. Very well. That same car crushes a young boy. Now, for many persons that is what I shall venture to call the intensive. The suffering, the agony, the lost hopes, the destiny changed, if not thwarted, are worth exactly such a sum. In France a certain phrase in

Latin covers these values. What is called the *pretium doloris* professes to correspond to the physical pain of the patient or patients. The other suffering — the moral suffering, if I may call it so — is still left outside the case, in virtue of a certain sense of the decencies, which, it is probable, will soon die out.'

'I beg pardon,' said Mr. Stone, 'do you prefer settlements that are inadequate, to be sure, but that are made in good faith, to debt in perpetuity? Pardon me, but if I clearly understand you, you reproach insurance precisely for what I regard as one of its greatest achievements; that is, contributing to compose, or at least to conclude, either with the assent of the parties concerned, or with the sanction of a magistrate, conflicts that threaten to perpetuate themselves in anger and hatred.'

'Mr. Stone, I'm willing to admit that that looks like a victory. Now, in the case of any victory, I like to remind myself of its cost. In spite of appearances, the genius of modern civilization is one of simplification. It pretends to harmonize the universe. Thus, for example, it tries to integrate the intensive with the extensive. Don't frown; you know now what I am trying to say when I employ those terms; modern genius does not despair of reducing the incommensurable world of the soul to definite material values. "Everything is worth so much," according to Thomas Pollock Nageoire, that American whom a great French writer has invented.'

'But,' exclaimed Mr. Stone, 'we've got to choose. Either "everything is worth so much," as you say — derisively, it seems to me — or else "nothing is worth anything," which seems to me absurd, and even to some extent criminal.'

'Don't believe, Mr. Stone, that I am one of those men who dream of keeping the tide from coming in. Like every one else I am insured against all sorts of calamities, faults, and follies. The difference between our ways of considering and accepting things lies in my trying always to see clearly where the current is carrying me. In the modern world any one who should refuse to take out certain forms of insurance would be condemning himself either to live like a larva or to run extravagant risks. I have therefore taken out many policies. I know that in doing so I acquiesce in the commercialization of certain moral values; that in doing so I depreciate and degrade them, that from the very fact that we are willing to assign commercial value to life and death, pain and pleasure, they lose a part of their human value, or, if the word doesn't disturb you, of their divine value, and lose, also, their majesty, their real greatness. I know that in buying my policies I undertake to escape all sorts of bothers and responsibilities. So I pay, Mr. Stone. I pay, and I am not duped. I understand that for many of my contemporaries insurance is a substitute at once for conscience — which is our guardian angel — for honor, for gratitude, and for many other things besides. Therefore it all makes me laugh, at least on the days when I can laugh. "The insurance company will pay!" Such is the magic formula in which is summed up the act of faith, the act of hope, and the act of contrition. Let's laugh, Mr. Stone. It's a touching business, this taste for security in a species that at the same time shows so strong a taste for risk. Oh, I should like to insure against mosquito bites, against colds in the head, against seasickness, against laziness, against blue devils, against doubt, against remorse, against grief, against jealousy, against anger, against love, and against friendship. If, like you, I were a religious man, I'd take out insurance on the existence of God, and more insurance on the reality of heaven. And what else besides? Against myself, against everything, and on everything!'

Mr. Stone closed an eye, which is his way of

smiling. 'You laugh, but what you say deserves thinking over,' said he.

'In that case, Mr. Stone, allow me to give you time to think this over too: insurance, which has been the burden of our conversation, belongs to that family of human inventions which tend to ameliorate individual and social life.'

'Quite so. And since I am less fussy than you, I regard that amelioration as attained.'

'Agreed, Mr. Stone. The amelioration is attained, but unluckily it is offset by certain consequences that to my mind are unfortunate, since they tend to demoralize the man whom insurance is designed to protect. You cannot fail to have observed that the same thing happens in the case of all sorts of institutions that yet were born of the idea of justice. In my own country, I remember the passing of the well-known law dealing with labor accidents. No law seemed more necessary, no law ever so satisfied the intellect, or even common-sense. The law has done great service in the cause of equity. Who would dream of denying it? On the other hand, it permits many interpretations and applications that the barest honesty would reject. This admirable, this indispensable, law has, to a certain degree and in the case of certain persons, bred a contempt of work and a taste for fraud. Admit that the fact is disquieting. It is the same, it will be the same, in the case of all other arrangements that in good faith aim at lightening man's burdens by raising not only what you call his "standard of living," but also, and more generally, his personal status. The great law of compensation governs the work of the legislator as it governs that of the man of science. We have learned that almost all scientific discoveries are big with a certain amount of good and with a notable quantity of evil. In every one of our thoughts there is what, if you will permit the image, I call the part of God and the part of the Devil.'

'We have to make up our minds to it,' said Mr. Stone, lighting a big cigar. 'Look, Monsieur Duhamel, this cigar will doubtless cause me a great deal of pleasure and perhaps a bit of harm.'

'Yes... No... Mr. Stone, that thought should at least incline us not to be too easily proud of our inventions. Man loves to attack the difficult thing...'

'Obviously, and then?'

'He ought to devote himself — not exclusively, but at any rate loyally — to the study of what I call non-reversionary values. Otherwise our civilization can be nothing more than a delusion.'

'What do you call non-reversionary values?'

'An old dream: ideas, rules, laws, and discoveries that it would be almost impossible to turn against man.'

Mr. Stone made no immediate reply. His forehead became furrowed, his eye cold. He looked at me as if he wished to hypnotize me, and I felt the approach of the moment when I should be obliged to buy some spring mattresses.

XIV

NOTES AND SKETCHES ILLUSTRATIVE OF THE WORLD AS IT IS TO BE

O CROSS-ROADS! O Cuvier! What next? Surely that next thing is humus, a compost of fifty nations that ask a moment of respite before giving up their ancient memories, all like coins that are to be melted down in the pitiless furnace, but that still show a striking head or two.

A hundred times a day I suffered from hallucinations, Emile Vandervelde kept a fur shop: there could be no mistake about it. Through what combination of circumstances did Einstein become the leader of an orchestra in Chicago? Twice already Pirandello had asked for my ticket in the Pullman car; he had been followed by a big Nubian who ordinarily would have been guiding travelers to the first cataract of the Nile. In the station at Pittsburgh, the giant, all smeared with coal dust, who looked at me scornfully from the cab of his engine, was — good Heavens, Vlaminck! Prince Haïdar Fazil was an employee of the Elevated; it was incredible, and it was true. Max Jacob had cashed my checks, he was sucking a gum-drop, and spat at short intervals into the corner of his cage. Jouvet — what a fate! — ran an elevator in the Times Square Hotel. M. Benès pretended not to recognize me, yet he was not ashamed to sell iced orange-juice on Sixth Avenue. I could not allow André Gide to open the taxi door and volunteer to carry my bag. I almost trod on the toes of Rabindranath Tagore near the Brooklyn Bridge; he wore his usual majestic and absent-minded expression. And M. Zaleski, with the greatest gravity, was regulating traffic. He arrested that chauffeur. Yet I am quite certain I saw Lenin dead — not only dead, but embalmed.

O American faces! O dream of the world as it is to be! All the people of the world touching elbows!

I met myself three times, and not in a mirror.

At the Pennsylvania Station a porter, majestic as a Cathedral verger, glanced an order at one of his minions to take my baggage.

I was not lost, I was not abandoned in this grim, bustling crowd that was noisy and taciturn at the same time. That sisterly, watchful glance, that glance which is so vivacious, so frank, I must say so French, and especially so easy to interpret, is that of — what shall I christen her for my friendly archives? — is that of, let us say Mademoiselle Greatheart.

'I am going to go up to your room,' she said, 'and see whether you're comfortably settled. I will give you your letters, and show you the ropes.'

We started. How the elevator flew! Following the bell-boy, we began our search for the room that was hidden so thoroughly in this labyrinthine building.

At last! The bell-boy lighted the lamps, put down the bags, and stood at attention. On his lips was a smile that I knew well, for I have often seen it blossom in this home of the tip. I understood. I took a quarter from my purse. The boy pocketed it, muttered an indifferent 'thank you,' smiled again, and did not budge. In three words, I gave him to understand that I was obliged for his services, but that he was free to depart. Then, bringing his heels together, laying his little finger along the seam of his trouser leg and fixing his gaze on space, the boy came to attention, and in an authoritative voice, that voice as of a loud-speaker that you imagine the voice of the Law to be, recited: 'The gentleman will please ask the lady to leave the chamber at once. Until the lady has left, the gentleman must leave the door open.'

Thereupon, he saluted, about-faced, and without closing the door, gained the hallway, where I heard him walking to and fro.

A gust of anger rose, swelled, and choked me. I had a keen desire to break something, a strong impulse to shout out at the top of my voice the word that in France expresses anger, despair, rebellion, and the resolution to die rather than surrender.

But Greatheart smiled. She had lived for a long time among these dragons of virtue. The vulgarity of the laws no longer made her blush. She obeyed and left. 'I will wait for you,' she said, 'in the hall on this story. There two friends may freely discuss their affairs.'

The same place, the next evening. I was leaving the bathroom, that fabulous bathroom which the economists and the sociologists vie in praising. It is the noblest victory of American pride.

It was warm. The radiator was having its last fit of the evening. I crossed the bedroom to get my pyjamas. Solitude, solitude!

Then suddenly the door, which by chance I had forgotten to lock, came open. A lady appeared in it — shingle, short skirt, rouge, powder, pearls, and diamonds.

She contemplated with interest the person

thus surprised in his privacy, and observed, with the completest calm, 'My mistake. Beg pardon.'

Would I not be thoroughly justified, I thought, in dragging that lady into court and demanding heavy damages? Oh, if I only had had witnesses! Oh, if only the bell-boy had been there, that vigilant guardian angel of my blushes!

The same place, five days later. Greatheart knocked at my door. She was laden with letters — news from home, sad news, for some one whom I loved was dead.

I was far from my native country, from my home, from my love. With my chin upon my breast, I gave myself up to bitter reflection. One who was part of my life was no longer anything but a memory. In my heart of hearts I found the world sad. Greatheart looked at me, and her eyes filled with tears.

Then suddenly the telephone rang piercingly. 'Hurry, Monsieur,' it said, 'hurry; grasp the receiver, and listen, listen!'

At once I recognized that puppet voice. Again the law spoke. 'We know,' it said, 'that a lady has entered your room. Be good enough to open the door and ask this woman, who is not provided with the special authorization, to leave at once.'

'Very well, my friend,' said I to Greatheart, 'let us go. I am not today in any condition to resist. I have not the least desire to laugh, but...'

'No, I do not own an automobile,' said Thomas W. Eaton. 'I am professor of English at the university. I am paid five thousand dollars a year. Don't translate the sum into francs, for that will not tell you anything. My wife is always ailing. I have two boys. I spend all I earn. There are Pullman-car conductors who are better paid than I. Don't believe that things here are as they are in Germany, where they bid against one another for the professors whom they want. Not at all, especially when we do not know how to advertise ourselves skillfully. The country has not yet emerged from the critical period in which a people gets its bearings. Will it ever emerge? Our nation, which is so big and so rich, does not fully comprehend the importance of certain things: art, for example, and literature. I am not what people call a malcontent. Certainly not; I love my profession. I am even ready to make sacrifices for it. Our city is small, in spite of its five hundred thousand inhabitants. At the university we have really handsome buildings; we have more stones than books. The college wants, first of all, the things that show. No, I don't complain. I shall even have a pension paid by the Rockefeller fund. I see what you're thinking: if Rockefeller had never lived... Oh, well, there would have been some one else. The pity of it is that, so far as we are concerned, charity must supplement the institution.'

Thomas W. Eaton went on speaking. His smile was ironic and sorrowful. He made me think of those intelligent, sensitive people who sometimes appear, no one knows how or why, in some parvenu family, and whose suppliant glances ask your indulgence. He talked for a long while. Sometimes his voice was lost in the clamor of traffic. I heard fragments of phrases: 'When a man earns ten dollars a day, the idea of getting no more than nine seems like a disgrace, almost like a suicide...' 'When a gentleman says that the social question is settled in his country, he means that it is settled so far as he is concerned...'

Thomas W. Eaton kept on talking. The traffic made so much noise that I could no longer hear anything at all.

I was walking along the sidewalk. High above me on the thirty-fifth story a Negro, with half his body hanging out over the abyss, was cleaning the windows of a building. For a moment I closed my eyes and hurried by.

My stomach began to feel empty. I did not like American food. Even the fruit, even the eggs, seemed to taste of machinery. The simplest dishes had an after-taste that suggested industrial by-products.

What did they sell in that shop? It was a big, long room, like a hall, that penetrated as far as you could see into the cliff-like building. In spite of the curtainless windows and a few lamps, the cavern seemed poorly lighted. Gradually my eye grew accustomed to the gloom, and I made out long rows of armchairs. Was it one of those places where they dispensed music? No. Was it a theater? No. Was it a gigantic boot-blacking 'parlor'? Not in the least. It was a restaurant.

All the rows of armchairs extended in parallel lines, and as in a theater each row was so arranged that the backs of the chairs were turned toward the next row. And the tables? There were no tables. The customer of these odd distributors of eatables goes to the end of the room, and gets a filled plate that he brings back to the seat he has chosen. The left arm of the chair is wide and flat, and shaped like a spatula. There the diner puts his plate and his bread.

He crosses his legs, gazes at the backs of the necks of the other customers, and with a melancholy jaw begins to masticate his food.

Little pubs of France, with your low-ceiled, warm, and smoky little rooms where three poor devils, packed tightly round a tiny iron table, can tuck away Burgundian beef, swap stories, play the flute, and be cheerful, blessedly cheerful... will you go too?

I looked again at the chairs with their broad, flat arms, whose deformity made you think of the suspicious apparatus you see in hospitals, and went on my way. Here were two, here were ten, other restaurants of the same kind. Was it, then, thus that the men of the future would eat? How desperately dull! I went on — and I was not hungry any more.

By way of letting in a little fresh air, let us shift the scene to a model farm in Alabama.

'We are going to show you our finest bull.'

He was a prince, almost a demi-god: his stable had all the air of a sanctuary. On seeing us, he lowered his head and uttered a frightful bellow that made the walls shake. A hot vapor was blown from his nostrils, which bore a stout iron ring. His impatient hoof scraped the concrete floor.

'But what,' said I, 'makes him so bad-tempered? We don't look so very terrifying.'

'Oh,' said the breeder, 'he was the most placid and reasonable of bulls. A child could have led him with a straw. One day he got into a fight and killed his adversary, a bull as handsome and as strong as himself. Ever since, he has been crazy with pride. He has grown too big for his boots. He no longer doubts himself. He knows what conquering is. He wants to conquer everything he sees.'

That is the supreme danger of success! As I left the model barn, I thought sadly of the great peoples whom glory suddenly intoxicates, of those great peoples who, alas, have no rings in their noses.

It was at dusk in late autumn; there was a dismal drizzle of rain, as if night itself were falling in fine drops. A van had just cast some pieces of furniture on the sidewalk. The stage was empty. The movers remained in the wings. The street contained only ghostly vehicles and phantom pedestrians.

The furniture? In the phrase of our cheerful dealers in antiques, it was not 'period.' It consisted of vague pieces without form, and perhaps without name, not exactly of wood, not necessarily of metal, but quite possibly of compressed paper, of imitation cardboard, of an agglomerate of dust. And yet life had already given them a faint human patina, the only touch of dignity in this flotsam. You recognized the parts of a bed, picture-frames of tarnished gilt, a bureau, a refrigerator like a coffin standing on end, a small herd of four-footed ghosts that were chairs and tables. At the center of this humble chaos, on the sofa between two little trunks, there was a kind of black box that sang, yes, sang, in funereal tones, the refrain of *Hit the deck*.

It was a wireless set that chance had started going, and that was telling what it knew, singing to itself alone among the disordered pieces of furniture, in the twilight under a rain that was thick with dust.

O voice of the world that is to be!

Here is a conversation that I overheard in Stevens Hall between two persons sunk in deep armchairs, persons whom I did not see, and who spoke without apparent emotion, in French:

'... No, he's not a Levantine, I assure you. And he's not a Jew. We must be just. I work with Jews here, people who are perfectly acceptable. He's a "hundred-percenter." Imagine — Smith! He is the Durand or Dupont of this country. This is only your first visit. You can't understand. It is a hard and humble life that makes people scrupulous — not this frenzied and extravagant prosperity. We French have made some blunders, dealing with these people. They're making us pay for them. They are growing stubborn. They are much too proud of their money, which all the same is not worth so much as all that! All this "business" is a damned bore. And the last of it, *mon cher* —! They will soon have no further need either for your models or for your instructions. You had better be quick if you want to sell them something, for in ten years you will be selling them nothing, ab-so-lute-ly nothing. You will not sell them even pictures by Rembrandt; they'll be making their own. Smith — I know Smith: he will surprise you yet. You are still at the stage of Cæsar Birotteau. But the sense of honor is something that soon changes. When Smith goes bankrupt, he is not dishonored. He starts fresh; he gets on his feet again. In fact, as things are now, you *can't* be dishonored. Here, you're not in a country where a man pays his father's debts. Admit that that is fair enough. Smith writes me a letter every now and then — one that is very important to our business, you understand — and it carries in one corner this subtle notice: "Letter signed but not re-read." That is expected here, it seems. I let myself be caught by it once. Now, I keep my eyes open. Well — there you are. The East is bigger than you think. It begins in the suburbs of Warsaw, swings round the globe, and does not stop till the middle of the Atlantic.'

Silence followed, and puffs of cigar smoke. Then there came this: 'The solemn moment in the history of the twentieth century is not the month of August, 1914, or the month of November, 1918. No. Take it from me: it is the moment when the home market became too small for the United States. And then the creature got up on its hind legs...'

It was midnight. I was returning to my cell in the Pennsylvania Station Hotel. Was I exhausted? Certainly! I was drunk with noise, with delirious lights, with brazen odors, and with humanity gone crazy. I was certainly exhausted, but yet I was upheld by a righteous fury of protest and rebellion.

To prove, at least to myself, that I had not been absorbed, that I did not acquiesce, that I had not let myself be won over, that I was not the dupe of this excessive and inharmonious civilization, that I was not the accomplice of this waste, of this rush, of this pride, I sought the inmost sanctuary of my soul, and questioned the shades of my ancestors.

'Inspire me,' I cried, 'O peasantry of France, you of the virtues that twist into oddities, you whom I have often laughed at, you whose whole history is patience, reserve, economy, and shrewdness, inspire me, for I am alone in the midst of this foreign people. My fathers, save me.'

And the help came. Solemnly for an hour, with a strong sense of accomplishing an act that might be useless but was at least symbolic, of challenging the immanent world, of declaring myself a rebel — solemnly, I say, I sat and mended the lining of my waistcoat, then washed my handkerchiefs in the wash-bowl, and put them to dry on top of the radiator. Then, purified and soothed, I went to bed, and slept an ethereal sleep.

Alas, in the middle of the night I awoke covered with sweat and in the grip of nightmare. I had dreamed that American gardeners, to simplify their business, reduce labor costs, push sales, and lower prices, had decided to standardize the flowers, and no longer grow any but a single species that was specially profitable, and that lasted well.

I had discovered an oasis.

To begin with, there was that small room opening on the 'campus' of a big college. A silence that smelt of boxwood unexpectedly evoked the grave peace of the Escurial. A young man was there among his books. 'Mind,' he said, and his voice had wings, 'cannot die. See how comfortable it is to work and reflect here. I feel so far removed from the encompassing world that, without even thinking of the matter, I have restored monastic discipline and the monastic cell. The very excesses of our civilization will produce anchorites. We must never despair...'

We left the street with its convulsive activity, and entered the ethnological museum. It was solitude itself, one of the least peopled places in the world. There was a strong odor of encaustics. It was a haven of peace. We walked a few steps, and what did we see? Huts of straw and boughs with the red embers of fires. Superb and silent warriors were smoking pipes. Women were cooking. In the distance was the enormous virgin prairie. Farther away rose the forest. There were lakes without boats, and rivers without mills. The hour that I spent there made me thoroughly homesick.

And what besides? A great public library. It

was orderly, rich, and hospitable. I was taken over it by a man with ardent eyes, who spoke in a hushed voice like a priest at an altar. Thousands of shadowy figures were at work there, in an atmosphere of almost religious fervor. A blessed living warmth heartened the traveler. It was a happy place. I was home again, and there were still refuges and friendly inns in a world less concerned to live than to rush towards death.

XV

MEDITATION ON THE CATHEDRAL OF COMMERCE

A BRISK breeze whose gusts made the slender building quiver had miraculously freshened the landscape. I felt young again: my eye was clear, my wits were sharpened.

Landscape! As far as the eye could see, there was nothing but the work of man; on the earth and under the earth, on the face of the waters, and in the depths of the sky.

Here was man as he is everywhere and always. Here was a people like all other peoples, with its grief and its joy, with its achievements and its virtues, which are not mean, with its temples, its philosophies, its idealists, its saints, its rulers, and its leaders.

My critic will rise, red with anger, and with his proofs in his hand will point out to me that I have not understood.

Yet I have given my life to gaining knowledge of man, to the love, to the defense, and to the praise of man. Have I made all the long pilgrimage of life only to meet this rebuff; that is, this failure to understand, this renunciation of my hopes? Have I written all my long chant of confidence in man only to end in refusing my adhesion? Last bitterness of all: I have failed to love.

Behind the first critic, I divine another. He smiles, and shakes his head. 'America,' he says, with a wink, 'is like a woman, like life, like the world. Everything that you can say of America is true, and the most violently contradictory thoughts and words have all some truth in them.'

America? I am not talking of America. By means of this America I am questioning the future; I am trying to determine the path that, willy-nilly, we must follow.

The naturalist who should try to make an imitation skull of celluloid, *galalith*, galvanized rubber, especially treated wood, or of any other of the strange materials that can be brought to imitate marble, or horn, or ivory, or bone, or rubber, or porcelain, or feldspar, would be wasting his time. A real skull with its cavities, its sutures, its processes, its apparent and its concealed structure, is cheaper than the most imperfect imitation.

The engineer who should apply himself to the task of putting together an apparatus capable of supplying in every spatial dimension the number of motive operations — I will demand no sensory perceptions — that we can ask of a human hand, who, confident in his methods, should undertake to join to his mechanism a directing organism, capable of ordering at the appropriate time two or three only of the hundred thousand combinations that the brain suggests to the muscles, and who, finally, should try to adapt this marvel to the needs of industry, would find that, even at modern wages, a healthy Negro would be more profitable than the automaton. A Negro with not one, but two hands, two feet, a back and a head supplied with sensory centers, would be a motor that, though yielding no more than twenty-five per cent of its potential energy, would be at least twice as good as the best apparatus.

In the serious and excellent work that André Siegfried has devoted to the United States, he seems to assign to mechanical achievement a strictly technical limit: 'No one,' he says, 'has yet invented a machine for picking strawberries.'

The complexity of technical problems is not enough to discourage the mind in a career that for more than a century has been signalized by intoxicating success. A machine for picking strawberries? Don't set the Americans that task, or, heavens, they will probably go and invent one! And perhaps they will also invent a machine to select the strawberries, and to taste and digest them. Have they not invented other machines, that, for example, which separates the hard little seeds from the cotton fiber? And have they not found a way to extract from that seed, an oil that passes for edible — that oil which makes a part of American food odious and even indigestible?

No: it is not complexity, but the competition of human beings that limits machinery. The machine retires from the field whenever, all things considered, it costs more than human labor.

I imagine American genius brought to bay before these barriers, and, as any generous man would do, I try to give it a free field. It seems evident that, once we know the method, we can keep on indefinitely inventing more and more delicate machines, fitted for more and more delicate action. Nevertheless, deprived of industrial consecration, machines will crumble away under the dust of museums. Machines that business cannot use are nothing but the amusement of the curious or of lunatics. The usefulness of the machine is limited by the very life that it imitates.

To the manufacturers, the merchants, and the lawmakers of the coming world whom this terrible problem will burden, I suggest a comparative study of the civilization of the animals that share our planet. On one hand, there are all the human civilizations, striving throughout thousands of years to conquer temporal and spiritual benefits; all those people suddenly enlightened through the inductive method, which in a single century transformed the face of the earth, destroyed traditions, and improvised new schemes. On the other hand, there are many species of animals, especially the insects, that are organized into powerful societies, with hierarchies, laws, methods, monuments, and, who knows? something better than a legend, perhaps a history.

In the United States, that far Western land which has already made us aware of the promises of the future, what strikes the European traveler is the progressive approximation of human life to what we know of the way of life of insects — the same effacement of the individual, the same progressive reduction and unification of social types, the same organization of the group into special castes, the same submission of every one to those obscure exigencies which Maeterlinck names the genius of the hive or of the ant-hill.

The essential difference between insect and human civilizations is that, whether for agriculture or breeding — which they practice with skill — for their surgery, their industry, or their architecture, insects seem never to have recourse to apparatus capable of prolonging, or supplementing, or multiplying the strength of the organs. They have invented neither tools nor arms. They have obtained everything from certain anatomical modifications. They have demanded laboratories, tools, and arsenals from their own physical structure. The troublesome question of occupations and social castes is solved by differentiations of structure. All their chemistry, which is not simple, and which is at once alimentary and therapeutic, industrial and military, remains an affair of glands and secretions. We have seen the feet, the mandibles, the antennæ, and the sting all transformed to meet the needs of a civilization that is none the less masterly because it often inspires us with an unconquerable terror.

It seems to me that if mechanical progress should some day find itself impeded, either by the play of economic laws or by any other inveterate obstacle, future society would certainly find inspiration in the insects.

At the point to which American genius has attained, it will almost surely be obliged to seek an outlet in that direction.

The biologists, even by continuing their experiments through more than seventy generations of an animal species, seem to have been unable to prove the inheritance of acquired characteristics. No matter! In a species so obstinately rigid in form as man, the evolution of organic characteristics is obvious and unmistakable, and under the powerful urging of sociologists and economists the men of science will soon trace the broad outlines of an experimental evolution. If America, in the strength of its immense resources, once offers the problem to competition, I do not doubt that in the course of the century, it will attain astonishing results.

If steel machinery refuses to make profitable progress, nothing remains except to turn to man, and modify the human machine. Breed, O America, the human tool, as you have bred the working ox, the milch cow, the laying hen, and the fat hog. Can you really do nothing with your hands and feet to supersede these costly, weak, and untrustworthy instruments? In a country where law is sovereign, can you not turn into inherited characteristics certain functions and certain trades that require some special physical attribute? Can you not engage in scientific human breeding and selection? Since you have already subjected certain specimens of humanity to sterilization, is it impossible for you to imitate the bees and the ants, and create a body of people, sexless, devoid of passion, exclusively devoted to the instruction, the feeding, and the defense of the city?

How can such dramatic if nightmarish visions fail to haunt the mind of the visitor while, in the wake of a chattering guide, he goes through a great factory?

The sense of dull boredom that all the books devoted to the Taylor System used to let me divine is nothing in comparison with the mortal sadness that hovers over the great American industries.

The guide explains everything, both that the workmen are contented, and that they are well treated, and proud of their achievements. Doubtless, they have to sacrifice certain personal satisfactions that workmen formerly found in the work itself, but in return they need not work so hard or so long. Doubtless, those who find themselves employed in the most monotonous tasks do not continue in them absolutely all their lives, and are shifted to a new job whenever the business permits. Doubtless, the sense of individual responsibility is greatly diminished, which you can interpret as a lightening of the burden. But the advantages of system, the salaries, the leisure, the comfort...

I did my best to listen to the twaddle, and when sometimes I did succeed in hearing it, it made me want to shrug my shoulders and to laugh — even in those melancholy regions.

What, after all, is the result of these prodigies of system, the subjection of the working-man to rule, these tricks of publicity, this dictatorship of business, this protective tariff, this niggardly counting of every minute, of every bit of gayety, and of every bit of sunshine? Is it not in the end the attainment of the highest cost of living in the whole world?

What is the result of all these astute economies, these miracles of simplification, this utilization of the least waste material, of dust, of shade, of all the by-products of every operation and of every idea? Is it not to attain more waste and dilapidation, waste of energy, of heat, of light, of water, of electricity, of paper, and of food? A scandalous spectacle of the great cities is the inconceivable way in which the left hand dissipates the treasure painfully gathered by the right.

The continent is immense and opulent. Everything is there in measureless quantity: gold, silver, iron, oil, petroleum, wood, meat, and plants in infinite variety. They have only to take what they need and use it. The Americans have everything, I think, except the lark — an unpardonable oversight on the part of the Creator. That being so, they grasp, and they plunder. The paradoxical result is that here more money is needed to buy a bit of bread, to sleep in a bed, and to have a place in the sun, than is needed anywhere else.

The foreigner, the Frenchman, who travels over this illimitable territory, will not anywhere see a word, a notice, or a direction written in his native tongue. Is it a lack of courtesy? Certainly not. Is it because America is too completely isolated from other nations? Perhaps. But, above all, it is because, in spite of the eager curiosity that at the present moment America evokes, it daunts the traveler. It requires that the tourist should have a fortune to waste. The result is that you meet there none but men of business, drawn thither by the dazzle of the almighty dollar.

The miserable multitudes that today make up the flesh of living America came because they were attracted by the same torch. They accepted everything in the hope of a better, freer, and more spacious life; they accepted exile, the long journey across the ocean, rigorous obligations, the severities of admission, and the misery of a fresh start. They had even to accept poor wages if they did not happen to be the workmen most needed at the moment, masons during a building 'boom,' or mechanics during the first enthusiasm over the automobile. They accepted the requirements of standardization, the ungrateful, anonymous labor, and the iron discipline.

And what has their new country given them in exchange for their sacrifices? It has given them new needs and new desires. The whole philosophy of this industrial dictatorship leads to this unrighteous scheme: to impose appetites and needs on man.

Most often these immigrants came from a simple land where the son could wear his father's cloak all his life long. America has given them the shirt that will not survive two launderings, the shoe that you throw away the minute a hole appears in it, because it is not worth cobbling — which, moreover, no one knows nowadays how to do — and the ready-made overcoat that is worn out in a winter and has to be replaced. These poor people came from a land where the orchards bear all kinds of fruit, infinitely varied and rich in innumerable savors. America has taught them that if they are to get a good return, they had much better raise no more than two varieties of apples and one 'variety' of pear, if the word 'variety' will permit such abuse.

Do luxury and comfort come from such things? I was born in a land that by its soil, its inhabitants, and its achievements is diverse, motley, variable, and ingenious. We French know how to make out of milk, that simple and elementary food, more than a hundred kinds of cheese — all good, wholesome, sound, substantial, and pleasing. Every one of them has its history, its affinities, its particular rôle. In that one characteristic fact I recognize and admire the genius of my country; through that one fact I understand why it has produced so many great men in every walk of life.

For a French woman at home the supreme luxury is to wear a hat that is the only one of its model in all Paris. The supreme comfort is not necessarily the unsatisfying American bathroom that is introduced into every phase of the discussion; the supreme luxury is silence, fresh air, real music, intellectual liberty, and the habit of joyous living.

I belong to a community of peasants who for centuries have lovingly cultivated fifty different varieties of plum, and who find in each a taste deliciously unlike that of any of the others.

Well, no one in America concerns himself about

such delicate riches. The beings who today people the American ant-hills have no desire for these unsubstantial viands. They demand palpable, incontestable wealth, recommended, or, preferably, prescribed, by the national divinities. They yearn desperately for phonographs, radios, illustrated magazines, 'movies,' elevators, electric refrigerators, and automobiles, automobiles, and, once again, automobiles. They want to own at the earliest possible moment all the articles mentioned, which are so wonderfully convenient, and of which, by an odd reversal of things, they immediately become the anxious slaves.

They have not enough money; not enough money even now? No matter! The principal thing is to keep selling, even on credit, above all, on credit! American commerce knows how unceasingly to push back the limits of the market, unceasingly to put off till the morrow the threatening saturation-point. And all America goes into debt with ardor so that America may be enabled to sell something more. What beautiful devotion!

Seek the happiness, the well-being, the bliss, that results from these methods among the people who jostle you in the streets of New York or of Chicago; read it in their faces. Discover that ineffable satisfaction which is engendered by the rationalization of labor, by a watchful legislature, by the sharing of immense natural wealth, by the enjoyment of universal comfort, by the habit of sport, and by the play of scientific toys — seek it in the contracted foreheads, in the jaws, like the jaws of beasts of prey on the hunt, and in the eyes that remind you of those of a tired animal.

Thanks to incessant immigration, the human types are still varied: many of the newcomers still preserve their original beauty or charm; but a uniformly dejected expression has settled on these worried crowds. If the men are still different in feature, in figure, in carriage, and in gesture, they no longer have any but one and the same thought. They no longer have any but a single, violent desire.

The satisfaction of that desire seems daily to become harder to attain. We are no longer in the legendary time when, helped by the least luck, any resolute adventurer could succeed in pulling out a plum from the appetizing pie. America is growing old; it is even growing old quickly. Fortune is stabilizing. The golden flood is dyked, canalized, and carefully distributed. The number of new arrivals is regulated; they are chosen from among the best.

To inspire the multitude with patience, they still display from time to time, on the covers of illustrated magazines or on the screen of the cinema, a specimen of this prehistoric species: the man in the street who after twenty years of intense labor has become a multi-millionaire. That fabulous monster is no more than a painted fraud.

Because the man in the street begins to understand that he may well die on this ungrateful soil before he has realized the most modest of his dreams, and because in spite of everything he cannot abandon all chance of compelling fortune — he gambles; that is, he trades in securities, in commercial paper, and in foreign exchange; he speculates, and 'takes a flier' in the stock market. The misfortunes and bankruptcies of the European nations have fed this passion. The hotel waiter, the barber's apprentice, the bank clerk, the clerk in the dry-goods store, the janitor, the elevator-boy, and the bootblack all still have a vague hope of rising from the depths, thanks to some happy speculation.

Then, as happened in the autumn of 1929, there rises from time to time a storm that sweeps away all the papers and all the illusions, cleans the whole jungle, and brings quivering to the ground, pell-mell, the chattering multitudes of the amateur pirates.

There are many who take no part in the game. There are those who hope for nothing more than to eat each day something edible, and to sleep each night under a roof. If you care to see some examples, take a seat in the Subway or in the Elevated, between midnight and one o'clock in the morning.

In front of you there are ten old fellows of indeterminate age and with no appearance of life. They would pass well enough for ghosts. Where are they going? From what morose hell have they come? Their features are sunken and drawn as if they had been subjected to torture. With closed eyes, they doze, thrown one against another by the swaying of the car. Almost all of them are chewing gum as they sleep: any one would think that this movement of chewing was that involuntary trembling of the jaw which during severe famines you can see in the dying. Sometimes one of them spurts a long white streak of saliva on the floor, in contempt of comminatory notices. Sometimes one of the miserable creatures opens his eyes, and rests upon you a look full of despair, of hate, or of boredom.

They are not the legendary workmen who, as all the world knows, receive a hundred dollars a week, and who consecrate to the 'movies' all the time that they do not pass among the delights of the standard factory. They are those who people the hideous quarters of Brooklyn, or those miserable suburbs that stretch as far as the eye can reach along the plain of Chicago.

In brilliant New York I have seen as many beggars as I saw in Moscow. I have seen wandering along the frenzied streets the strange old scarecrows who, on some evening of especial boredom and disgust, spend their last pennies for an old soap box, mount it at the corner of a square, utter a few vague words of sedition, and who then, if they are not yet citizens of the promised land, and, as such, reserved for different treatment, are locked up, conducted under sufficient guard to the port and generously supplied with a third-class ticket to take them back across the ocean.

Of what account are the avenues that look like deep streams of wealth flowing between illuminated banks! Of what account are the mountainous buildings that evening crowns with flame! Of what account are the docks overflowing with merchandise, the railway stations stuffed with trains like ranged artillery, the factories, the banks, and the palaces! Of what account is all that!

'Here,' an American magistrate admitted to me, 'here, when a man is poor, he is poor indeed.'

'The American,' said Thomas S. Baker, 'is in a hurry to achieve a life that shall be free of all irksome work.'

That is true. These millions of bolts are made by the turning lathe? But what of the turning lathe? That is made by another machine. And that other machine? By man, man whose irksome labor is necessarily the base of everything. Why, then, should we deceive ourselves about the significance and the purpose of machinery? Man is always in the mine, always in the quarry, always in the sewers, always in the stoke-hold of the steamship. With his pick he always makes the break in the oven where the molten iron is boiling. He is always present on the fifty-eighth story to place the last block and seal the last joint. Is it well, is it honest, to try to deceive yourself about the importance of victories that leave the old problem with all its teeth, with all its claws, and with all its venom?

But what is it that we call irksome labor? Do machines do everything? What of the tired journalist who looks at the clock even as it strikes midnight, and who calls upon his courage for yet another idea, for yet another effort, for still another twenty lines? I assert that the pen between his fingers is heavier than the heaviest of pickaxes, and that no machine can alleviate that suffering. What of the doctor whom you drag from his first sleep after a long day of adventure and battle? His overcoat seems as heavy to him as a whole cask of oil. And nothing will relieve him.

You would say that a turning-lathe goes of itself. But does the workman who feeds and watches it make no effort? Does he not in some way wear out his nerves, his eyes, his patience? When evening comes, is he not tired and irritable, just as he used to be? Has he not merely changed the form of his fatigue? Does he not dream of other machines that will relieve him of the effort of lifting his arm, opening his hand, of taking a step to the right, and then a step to the left? Since machines exist, why not demand everything of them; why not ask that they relieve us of everything, even life?

In our rich and fertile Normandy I visited a farm supplied by an enterprising owner with every imaginable machine. The laborers never fail a single day to point out such or such a task that seems to them to call for the intervention of some machine. Soon they will have a motor to wipe their noses, another to scratch their backs, and still another to smoke their pipes.

But man always finds himself at a point where some terrible and mortal effort demands a man and nothing else. Always he has to be near the blast furnace; always he must blow the glass.

And yet a large part of the American people carry to the extreme this singular system that banishes from existence not only irksome effort, but effort of any sort, even agreeable. Not a step will they take in the street: the car waits at the door. Not a step will they take upstairs: the elevator is at hand. They will soon no longer know how to write. Will they use the typewriter? Not at all: they will use the dictaphone, until they can communicate their ideas with a wink, or find the secret of the transmission of thought. I want to sit down; some one must push a chair under me. I want to eat; some one must put food on my plate. I even hope that soon some one will chew it for me, for you know that the workman-ant takes into his stomach and predigests the food intended for the nobles of the ant-hill. And again, I find it tiresome to bathe myself, for while that is going on, I am neglecting my business.

Inconceivable are the contradictions of a thought that extols effort, glorifies it, and dreams of suppressing it — as if effort were not the very measure of life!

Thus, then, behold Western Europe gaping in

astonishment, if not in horror, between two experiments that are being carried on, one in Russia and the other in the United States. Travelers, economists, philosophers, and sociologists delight to compare these two experiments, to contrast them so that, thanks to the opposing theories, they may finally be able to obtain arguments and information.

The two experiments are not comparable. The Russian experiment is purely political and ideological. For a thousand interior and exterior reasons it is already compromised. Its responsible authors seem, moreover, to have it at heart to vitiate it, to surrender it to despotism, to defeat it, and to rob it of all consideration.

The other experiment overlaps the bounds of politics in every direction: it puts into play ethics, science, and religion; it does not merely describe itself as a form of government; it describes itself as a 'civilization,' a mode of living. It touches everything; it affects every act and every person. Yet in appearance it is simple; it presents to the people only images that are elementary, powerful, and seductive. If necessary, it can be expressed in a dozen precepts, whereas the Russian experiment rests in unstable equilibrium on huge doctrinaire treatises that no one in the world would ever think seriously of reading through.

The American experiment is triumphant, sure of the future. It is scarcely questioned. The whole world holds it in respect. Inasmuch as it goes on and is perfected, it is no longer an experiment, but a complete outfit of laws and regulations. For some persons it is a method; for others it is an Evangel.

Spread everywhere with infinite variations, the American system now has the whole world for its field. It seems — but it is no more than a seeming — compatible with every political system. It adapts itself to anything, takes charge of everything, and succeeds in everything. It is turning Soviet Russia itself into a colony, purely in virtue, if I dare say so, of its so clearly pointing the way.

The American system has the supreme virtue of all 'new truth': it delights the single-minded and enchants children. All the children whom I know reason like Americans when it is a question of money, of pleasure, of glory, of power, and of work.

If, as Barrès says, it is true that to insure social peace, 'the poor must have the sense of their weakness,' America can sleep tranquilly.

The great reason for that sublime security is not, in my opinion, legislation as stern as a fortress. Nor is it either armed force with its engines, its gas, and its poisons, or the public and private police with their storied achievements. The great reason I see is the inextricable complexity of the social organism, its dizzy rhythm, and its proportions, which are already beyond the comprehension of human intelligence.

A minister of the French Republic once said to me with a smile: 'This evening twenty resolute men could get possession of Paris; that is, of France; that is, of power.'

As for Moscow and Leningrad, which are no more than great villages, the thing is clearer still. Merely in passing through them, the traveler comes to understand the sudden attack, to discover the vulnerable points, and to reconstruct the first riot. But America, Chicago, New York! Show me the intelligence able to comprehend — I say thoroughly to grasp as a whole — this tangle of forces in action.

'Do you,' I asked the captain of a great steamship, 'identify yourself with your boat? Do your intelligence and sensibility travel as a matter of course through the steel beams to the very end of this enormous organism, as you know happens in the case of a pilot and his aeroplane, or of a driver and his automobile? Do you feel what is going on in the ship two hundred yards from here?' The honest fellow shook his head. 'No,' said he, 'I experience what you describe in smaller boats, but this one goes beyond the capacity of any one mind. It is out of scale.'

So it is with everything. Suppose that the *Grande Armée* is falling to pieces, and that the genius of Napoleon no longer succeeds in giving life to that disportionate body even to its feelers. The *Grande Armée* would then no longer be within the scope of a single man.

What shall we say of America, that incredible swollen gland? It is no longer within the scope of the minds that created it. No one can any longer form any effective and clear idea of it. God himself...

This people is caught in the meshes of a machine, of which soon no one will know the secrets — the king-bolts, the vulnerable zones, the vital centers.

Contemplating the twenty elevators of a building, I asked, 'What would you do if the electricity gave out?'

'Oh,' was the reply, 'we are connected with three different generating plants.'

And what of the progress — that progress which is comparable to inertia — of this mass that rolls on no one knows toward what, through a sort of vehement habit!

The civilization of ants extends over the continents from the cold of the North to the cold of the South. Perhaps here and there there is some palace revolt. But the civilization of the ants has lasted for centuries on centuries. There are no revolutions among the insects.

No revolution in the American ant-heap can be imagined — unless indeed some day without any one's knowing why, without any one's foreseeing it, without any one's succeeding in explaining it after the event, the incredible machine goes off the track, collapses, and falls in cinders. For in the case of man, you never know.

America may fall, but American civilization will never perish; it is already mistress of the world.

Are we also to be conquered, we people of ordinary lands?

I have seen the strangest 'Americanisms' in Germany, that country where the young men on returning from their first trans-Atlantic trip, speak of New York as 'not bad, but not American enough.' In the wake of the architects I visited the new city of Frankfort, a city of blocks that in their monotony were like white chalk cliffs inhabited by disciplined little animals.

There are on our continent, in France as well as elsewhere, large regions that the spirit of old Europe has deserted. The American spirit colonizes little by little such a province, such a city, such a house, and such a soul.

How can the universe avoid being dazzled? Behold, people of Europe, behold the new empire! It has had two centuries of success, a constant rise; few wars, all of happy issue; it has kept its many problems at a safe distance; it feels the pride of being a numerous people, rich, feared, admired, a pride that begins to stir in the humblest passer-by, lost in the corridors of the ant-heap, a pride that is capable tomorrow of delivering a hundred million souls to the enterprises of their intoxicated leaders.

The sky was torn over Jersey City. A blazing ray of sunshine lighted Manhattan, and moved like a pointing finger over the strange buildings that seemed like curious, complicated, bewildering toys. It sparkled on a hundred thousand office windows, whose panes bore dizzy signs that represented struggle or victory, and that rose, rose, moved by a single impulse, stirred by a single inspiration.

The wind freshened. Under my feet the building trembled throughout its height, a tuning-fork of steel, brick, and cement. The chimneys disguised by the ornaments of the spire exhaled a mortal incense, the poisonous gas that, eight hundred feet below, the machinery of the subcellar was distilling.

I wanted to pause yet a little while to savor the unspeakable bitterness of being unable to love what I saw.

What was lacking in this people to keep it from being really great, the bearer of a great message, deserving honor, respect, and admiration? What was lacking to that glory? Great misfortunes, doubtless, and great trials, the terrible adventures that ripen a nation, turn it back upon itself, make it cherish its real treasures, squander its finest fruits, and discover its true path?

If I thought that this civilization were the carrying on of that which, in spite of many errors, has for thirty or forty centuries enriched the heritage of the species, how heartily would I not sing its praises? But where others see a continuation, I see a deviation, I find a breach.

If I thought that Europe, exhausted by its misfortunes and its crimes, had on the other side of the Atlantic a fervent posterity consecrated to the ancient cause that so many great men have served... But what! After more than two centuries you can still count on the fingers of your hand those representatives of this new society to whom we care to offer a place in our heart, and in our Pantheon!

And even if I believed that our European civilization had fulfilled its purpose, that it had exhausted its ambitions, and completed the sum of its achievements... But that, I do not believe.

FINIS